Skylark

by

Susan Hutchins

Skylark

Text Copyright
© 2020 Susan Hutchins
All Rights Reserved

British Library Cataloguing-In-Publication Data
A catalogue record of this book is available
from the British Library.

ISBN 978-1-9160531-5-1

Published via pgprintandofficeservices.co.uk

Acknowledgements

I would like to thank: Tim and Tracey Rhys, who encouraged me to write this story; Jo Beech for being there at the start; Paula Good for her hard work copy-editing and proofreading to make 'Skylark' a book to be proud of; and Chris Dart of Dartworks.design for his beautiful book cover. I give a big thank you to all my family and those friends that have patiently helped and listened while I was writing this story.

Prologue

February 2004

We are all here – Bill, Chris, Diane, Alice, Kate, me and, of course, Sean. He came to stay with me on the fifth of November, an easy date to remember; it's also our wedding anniversary. It's now the twenty-third of February. During these past months, he's become thinner and weaker by the day; like his body, his life is fading fast. I know it won't be for much longer. In the past week he has seldom left his bed. Even Lily, our Burmese cat who enjoyed the privilege of sharing the bed, has been banned from the room; the weight of her body on his legs made it difficult for him to move, and she is such a small cat.

Sean hasn't played his fiddle for over a week and the 6.00 p.m. cigarette and the half bottle of wine we share has become more habit than enjoyment; such a contrast to the old days, when Sean would say, 'Come on Annie! Let's get rat-assed!' and I would sneak off to bed leaving him glassy eyed, before he collapsed across the table.

Two days ago, I rang Bill and Sean's stepmother, Chris, to tell them I thought Sean's life was nearing its end; this time I was sure it wasn't a false alarm. Bill and Chris caught the next train to Bristol and arrived at my house later that day.

I rang Diane this morning. I told her Sean's condition had deteriorated and she's decided not to go into work. She's subdued. She'd been with us last evening and upset Bill when she prevented him from going into Sean's room. It was the only time I'd shown any anger towards her. Patrick – Bill's youngest son – had been killed by a speeding car when he was seven, and now he is losing Sean. I'd put my arm around Bill, led him into Sean's room and, as I did, I whispered to her, 'Wild horses wouldn't keep me from my daughter if she were dying.'

I understand it must be hard for her, that Sean, the man she considered to be her partner, wanted his estranged wife to nurse and care for him, and that his parents and our daughters, Alice and Kate, agreed it was the best thing for him.

Last night the nurses arrived just before midnight. They left about twenty minutes later, leaving Sean with the pump administering the morphine that now runs through his veins. I went to the bedroom window, stood watching them drive away before going back to Sean and rolling what was to be his last cigarette. When his eyes began to close, I took the cigarette from his fingers, put it in the ashtray. As I did, he looked at me with huge green eyes and said, 'I'm frightened.'

I wanted to tell him, 'So am I,' but, trying to appear strong, I merely squeezed his hand, held it until he fell into a deep sleep.

The room was cold – I'd turned off the radiator because of Sean's high temperature. When I was sure he wouldn't wake, I gently took my hand from his, pulled a duvet around my shoulders and lay down on the floor waiting for morning to arrive. When it did, Sean still remained in his deep sleep.

Sean's breathing is heavy and laboured. Alice and I move close to him. Kate, Chris, Bill and Diane move back against the wall. I smoothe Sean's lovely black hair, now streaked with grey, and whisper, 'We're all here; we all love you.'

I hear Bill say, 'He's going, he's going.' One last breath and I pick up the corner of the sheet and wipe away the blood that runs from Sean's mouth – such dark red blood.

'He's dead,' says Bill.

I look at Sean's empty body. For a few moments we stand in silence. Someone pulls open the door. Lily comes into the room. We leave while she weaves her way towards Sean.

What happens when something as monumental as the death of someone close to you occurs? Nothing reflects the enormity of the event. Inside there is numbness while all around everything returns to normal very quickly. The clock carries on ticking and life goes on in quite an ordinary way, except it's a life without Sean. We sit around the kitchen table while Chris, solid and sensible, puts the kettle on and makes tea. She says a few words; we are all lost in our own thoughts. She puts a mug in front of me, saying, 'You'd better call the doctor, love,' and I stand up.

By the time I return to the table the atmosphere has changed; the ritual of drinking tea has brought them together. We talk of mundane things: the weather; Chris's grandchildren; my grandchildren; anything but Sean. The bell rings and I put my tea down.

This will be the first time Dr Esler has entered Sean's room. Sean had always insisted on being up and dressed for his visits, but this visit is different; Sean is no more. He'll be one less patient on the list. The cursor moves closer to Delete. Sean's name is about to go into the tray marked 'Out'.

The doctor follows me up the stairs. I stand aside to let him into the room. Lily is curled up on Sean's chest – she opens one eye, fixing us with a wary amber stare, mewing her protest as I pick her up and put her down onto the floor.

The doctor's examination is brief. No conversation to be had with Sean today – just a few words to me as he fills out his forms. I follow him down the stairs. 'Thank you, doctor – goodbye.' Closing the door behind me, I put Esler into my tray marked 'Out'.

I am helping the nurse lay out Sean's body. Lily watches from the dressing table, her tail twitching. She's angry – she didn't want to be moved, she wanted to stay on Sean's body, to be left to say goodbye in her own time, in her own way.

Alice is with us; I have mixed feelings about her being here. Sean wouldn't want her to see him naked. He was always self-conscious of his body; kept it covered from the neck down, thinking he was too thin for shorts, bathing trunks, sleeveless tops. He could never see the beauty in his own slim, graceful form. I have to remind myself that he is no longer here and, if he is, I hope he understands that she feels the need to be part of this last act of caring for him.

I asked Diane if she wanted to be with us. I asked because Sean would have wished me to. I'm glad she said no.

The nurse and I are removing Sean's pyjamas, replacing them with clean ones. His body is unyielding – so awkward, so unlike him. He was always independent, even during his illness. The only time he asked for help was the night before last. I heard a thud; he called my name. I found him on the bathroom floor. I helped him up and into bed. He told me he'd had terrible diarrhoea and asked if I would check to make sure he had cleaned the toilet thoroughly. It was spotless.

We have finished. The nurse, efficient and cheerful, is pleased with our results. Sean, eyes closed, face washed, hair neatly combed, pyjamas buttoned to the collar, is clean and tidy, ready for his journey. I say goodbye to the nurse. Click, another player leaves.

I sit on the sofa, 'Yellow Pages' on my lap. Undertakers – so many! I recognise the 'Co-op', remembering the store from my childhood, even my mum's dividend number, 1279. She trusted them, and I pick up the phone.

Sean's escorts arrive within twenty minutes. I open the door to a pair of dark-suited, middle-aged men. Pale faces, formal, polite, straight from the 'Very Serious School for Undertakers'.

We enter Sean's room. Lily sits like a sentinel on Sean's chest. I gently remove her, holding her warmth close to me, taking comfort from the softness of her fur.

They put Sean into a black zip-up bag and transport him from the house. Lily and I watch from the window as his body is wheeled down the path and out into the street. Their van is parked in the middle of the road. The little Victorian houses were built without garages, so parking spaces are scarce. We watch as Sean's body is put into the van. The van drives away. Lily struggles away from my arms and walks out of the room.

I continue to look out of the window. Next-door's children arrive home from school. The lively sound of their chatter is interrupted when Diane calls my name. I turn to see her standing in the doorway with my spare set of keys in her hand. Hostility is in her voice when she says, 'I'm going.' I go over to her and take the keys. Another player is about to leave. One I will be glad not to see again. I don't have to pretend anymore. Don't have to pretend that I didn't mind that she slept with my husband in my bed; that he spent his last birthday and Christmas with her. She leaves the room. I hear her feet descending the stairs, the front door open and close. I watch her walk down the street, her sleek, dark, well-groomed hair. The smart, black coat tightly belted around her curvaceous frame. It won't be the last time we meet. Sean's words come back to me, 'Make sure she's okay. Try and be her friend – it won't be easy, but try.'

I gather together the blood-stained sheet, Sean's duvet, his pyjamas and pillows, take them outside and put them into the bin. Sean has been wrapped, packed and sent away but I know, without a doubt, that whatever reminders I cast aside, they will remain with me, inside my head, following every footstep I take.

I meet Bill on the garden path. He is carrying three bottles of red wine. 'All right, duck?' he says. 'I thought we could all do with a drink.'

Teacups are exchanged for wine glasses. Chris has made sandwiches, dainty with cheese and cucumber. We laugh and joke as we drink. There is a party atmosphere. The kitchen has become a stage but I don't know whether I'm player, audience or wooden puppet. The party continues until the bottles are empty. Bill looks tired. He gazes into his empty glass, staggering as he stands up from the table mumbling that he is going to bed. He stumbles from the room.

A hush has fallen. Chris's voice drifts into my frozen mind. 'I feel exhausted,' she says. 'I'll go and see how Bill is. I think I'll probably join him.'

The harsh clink of glasses as she collects them from the table and puts them onto the draining board tells me in uneven chimes that the day is coming to a close. Alice rises from the table and, in her quiet voice, tells me she has to go. I stand up, put my arms around her and lay my cheek against her copper curls. I don't think I could have managed without the support she has given me. I had only to pick up the phone and she would be by my side, bringing the children with her if she needed to. She was a shoulder to cry on; someone to sit with Sean when I needed to go out. I only had to ask; it was more than I deserved. Alice is thirty-three, but her small, fine-boned frame feels child-like in my arms. Her clear grey eyes reflect her concern. 'Are you all right?' she asks. 'I'll call round in the morning after I've taken the children to school.'

'That would be nice. Granddad and Chris would like to see you before they go, but don't worry, I'm okay.'

My daughters have never been close. The four years between them have given them different interests and friends; now, bonded in their grief, they embrace at the open door. Kate and I watch as Alice walks down the path. A mist has fallen, wrapping its way around her like a shroud as she disappears into the night.

Closing the door, I look at my younger daughter. Tall and slim like me, with her father's dark thick hair and beautiful green eyes. They are alike in so many ways, temperamental and easily offended, impatient when things don't go their way. But however cross I felt towards them, their intelligent quick wit would soon bring a smile to my face.

A deep hurt lived inside both Sean and Kate. Sean had never allowed me in to soften his pain, only alcohol was allowed to do that. Both were emotionally damaged. I understand the reasons for Kate's suffering. She had craved her father's affection since she first became aware of him. So had I, but I'd learned long before she was conceived that there was a wall inside him that kept any feelings of love and affection firmly wrapped. I can only guess at what had happened to Sean before his mother walked out on them, leaving Bill alone to bring up ten-year-old Sean and six-year-old Patrick. Neither Bill nor Sean would talk about her. The only reminder of her existence were the holes in the photographs where she had been removed.

Since Sean moved back into the house, a close and intimate affection developed between Kate and her father. Whenever Kate had a spare moment she would bring her flute and she and Sean would flood the house with jigs and reels. Their love of music brought them together, brought joy into the house, brought peace into their relationship. I'm glad Kate made that connection. I hope it will help her in her grief.

She turns to take her coat from the hook. 'I must be going as well,' she says. 'I'm on an early tomorrow and I mustn't be late. We're so short-staffed on the ward.' She comes towards me to kiss me goodbye.

I need to speak now. I have such a favour to ask. I know I shouldn't involve her, and I'm ashamed to ask, but he needs to know. Even the thought of saying his name causes guilt to rush through me.

'Please,' I say, 'before you go, will you do me a favour? Will you ring David? Tell him your dad died today. I don't want to speak to him. I'm sorry, but I can't...'

She looks at me. I lower my eyes. I feel her hesitate then she says, 'Yes, okay. What's his number?'

I tell her the number I know so well then I walk into the kitchen, closing the door behind me. The call is brief; Kate opens the door. I don't ask what was said. I don't want to know. We embrace in the hall. 'Thank you,' I whisper.

'I'll give you a ring tomorrow, Mum. Say goodbye to Chris and Granddad for me.'

The mist has lifted, but the night feels damp as I walk with her to her car. I wait while she starts the engine. The car moves away and I watch her tail lights disappear as she turns at the bottom of the road.

I go into the kitchen. Lily has returned to her favourite spot and is asleep on the shelf above the radiator. I switch off the light and darkness and time closes over the room.

I stand before my reflection in the bathroom mirror. I shall be sixty in May, and it shows. The grey is revealing itself through my dull brown hair. I've been in too deep for crying and the bags underneath my eyes are heavy with unshed tears. Such a sad face on the elderly widow.

Bill and Chris have my room, but I can't bring myself to sleep in Sean's room. I pick up my night clothes and the duvet from the floor where I'd left them and carry them down to the sitting room sofa.

The curtains are open. I draw them, banishing the night from the window. My body feels the chill of the cold room as I hurry into my pyjamas. I turn off the light and lay on the sofa, wrapping myself in the duvet. I can't get comfortable; the sofa's far too short for my long legs. I stretch them over the sofa's arm. It's only 9.30 p.m. Last night I had little sleep and the past few days have been very stressful. I thought sleep would come easily. I look around the dimly lit room. The light from a street lamp shines through a chink in the curtains, highlighting a photograph of my mother as she sits in the spotlight on the small stage of the sideboard.

I wish she were here. I would ask her how she coped after my father's death. How hard it must have been for her. Six happy years of marriage and then his sudden tragic death that left her to bring up two small daughters alone. She was convinced he would be waiting for her in heaven and was looking forward to their reunion. I hope she was right. If not, what a waste. She spent fifty years leading what she considered to be a good life, never straying once from her narrow celibate existence. She lived a life of neat perms, polished shoes, spotless oven, church every Sunday; not one swear word ever passed her lips during those years. A stroke sent her hopefully into his arms two years ago, unless he'd got fed up with waiting and had flown off with some other sort of angel.

Where is Sean? Is he playing his fiddle in some heavenly pub, where red wine flows from fountains? I know he wouldn't want to listen to harps, nor would he want angels for companions.

Can he see me? Can he read my thoughts? Does he know I will never forgive myself? I've asked myself over and over again, why I did what I did, why I ran with no thought or care for anyone or anything except my own beating heart and the excitement welling up inside me. Can he hear me? Can he catch the 'sorry, sorry, sorry...' left floating in the air?

CHAPTER 1

August 1997

I open the curtains to a fine morning; cumulus clouds are drifting across the sky towards the west. In five hours, we'll be flying above them, chasing them across the sea to Ireland. Usually we take the overnight ferry; I'll miss joining the line of passengers on the deck as the boat makes its way to Cork harbour; watching the passing picturesque villages and the Neapolitan-coloured town of Cobh give glimpses of a land of Guinness and peat fires, music and dance.

We've a lot to pack into the next two weeks – which is why we're flying. We're house hunting, searching the West coast of Clare and Galway to find the affordable property we hope to buy. Packed with our luggage, alongside our camping gear and Sean's fiddle, are a pile of house details sent from the Irish estate agents we've been in contact with.

I leave the window and go to the lump in the bed; giving it a gentle prod, I ask, 'Do you want a cup of tea?'

The lump grunts, which from experience means yes. Excited at the prospect of the trip, I hurry downstairs humming snatches of 'Fly Me to the Moon'. I switch on the television, put the kettle on to boil and grab a tin of cat food. Lily is mewing around my legs telling me to hurry. I'm only half listening to the newsreader when suddenly I'm jolted from my chores. Had I heard right, Princess Diana dead? Walking towards the television with the open tin of cat food in my hand, I listen... *She was pronounced dead at 4.05 this morning...*

Lily's crying has become incessant; I quickly feed her. Diana had been involved in a high speed car crash in Paris. Her companion, Dodi El Fayed, also died. The news has shocked me. I go back upstairs, put Sean's tea on the bedside table and tell him what's happened. Receiving no reply, I lift a small fraction of the duvet. Sean's half-open eye squints into the light.

'What did you say? Who died?'

He sits up, gropes for his tobacco and papers, rolls a cigarette and listens as I relate the news.

Although neither of us are particularly interested in royalty or celebrities, it certainly diverts our attention, though not for long. Diana's death becomes insignificant as we prepare to leave; after all, we're about to embark on a life-changing journey.

We both have our own reasons for buying a house in rural Ireland. Sean's is undoubtedly his passion for Irish music. Mine is the dream of a country life with time to garden and pursue my love of landscape painting; but, more importantly, I want Sean to be away from Bristol, away from musicians who seem to think that playing music and getting drunk go hand in hand. I want to move away from the local pubs and numerous off-licences within walking distance of our house. To put it in a nut-shell, I want Sean to drink less.

Our luggage is stacked in the hallway. Sean is in the kitchen with Lily asleep on his lap. Cigarette smoke carries the words when he says, 'She's upset; she knows we're going away.'

I want to tell him she'd hardly be sleeping if she was upset. Instead I say, 'She'll be fine. Jean's going to call in twice a day; you know how fond she is of her.'

With one hand stroking the cat, the other holding his cigarette, Sean looks unconvinced. Hearing Kate's car pull up and the beep of the horn, I'm relieved to say, 'Kate's here.' I give her a wave from the window. 'Come on. Let's get going.'

All the way to the airport Kate talks of nothing but Diana - 'How can something like that happen? It's shocking... awful... dreadful... her poor boys.'

I nod my head, murmuring a few appropriate words.

Sean gazes out of the window, his thoughts elsewhere.

Airports usually bustle with excitement; today is different. Diana's death has brought people together; condolences float above the crowd.

'...it's hard to believe...'

'...such a lovely woman...'

'...terrible, terrible...'

I whisper to Sean, 'Thank God we're going away. This will have died down when we get back.'

'Don't think we're gonna escape; the Irish love a good death. They'll really get their teeth into this one.'

We hire a small blue Fiat, leave Dublin airport and follow the signs to Athlone. A few miles after we leave the city, we see a brightly painted sign advertising coffee and hot food. We pull onto the garage forecourt. I get out of the car and push open the shop door. The smell of roasting chicken, a heated glass cabinet displaying an array of hot food makes me hungry. I cast my mind away from the food. We can't hang around long; we've a four-hour journey in front of us. We've booked a camping spot in Doolin, a small village on the West coast of Clare; we don't want to be putting up the tent in the dark.

I pick up two bars of chocolate and ask the middle-aged woman who comes to serve me for two coffees. She returns with the coffee and with a look of concern says, 'I'm sorry for your troubles.'

'What troubles?' I ask, puzzled.

'Princess Diana. Terrible. Terrible.'

Once upon a time, Doolin was a quiet, out of the way place. It's now a transit camp for lovers of Irish music. Most visitors arrive by a bus that drops them outside a large purpose-built hostel and campsite. When they've settled, the majority of campers head for the sanctuary of O'Connell's pub, which is where Sean and I go after erecting our tent on a soggy field in the rain.

We squeeze into O'Connell's, shove our way through wet anoraks and damp woolly jumpers, breathe air heavy with cigarette smoke and the sweet smell of Guinness, and join the throng of people that queue for the bar. Somewhere in the room, hidden beneath laughter and chatter, comes the faint sound of Irish music.

We move slowly forwards. Next to the pump, glasses of Guinness wait to be topped-up to the brim. We make room for two well-built blonde men, each of them carrying two full pints. One of them stops to take a sip, leaving creamy foam on the hairs of his moustache. He shouts to his mate in a language that may be Swedish, laughs and slops liquid onto the already sticky floor.

We arrive at the bar; the till is so jammed with bank notes it won't shut. A man with an American accent shouts, 'What time's closing?'

'The thirty-first of October,' shouts the barman.

After what seems like twenty minutes we leave the counter, Sean clutching his fiddle and a pint of beer, me following with a half of lager. Trying not to spill them, we push our way to the corner where the music is coming from.

The musicians are huddled together like pilgrims taking communion with pints of Guinness and a mantra of Irish music; shoulders touch shoulders; the boys on bodhrans bend over their goatskin drums like old men with their elbows shackled. The accordion player has put his instrument under the table.

There's no room for Sean to sit and play. Playing and drinking is one of the reasons he's here and the queue to the bar is even more uninviting. 'Let's go,' he says. Without waiting, he downs his drink and pushes his way to the door. I leave mine on the table, glad to be going.

The weather has been whipped to a storm; a strong west wind pushes the rain across the field. Sean shelters in the washroom, having a last cigarette. I hurry into the night looking for the tent. The wet penetrates my shoes. I curse myself for not bringing water-proof boots and a torch. It's difficult to avoid the numerous guy ropes and I'm worried one trip will release a tent and send it on a merry dance.

Glad to see the tent is still standing, I unzip it, crawl through the flapping wet nylon, disentangle myself from my damp clothes and grope my way into my sleeping-bag. Soon I hear Sean struggling with the zip. Cursing the weather, he heaves himself through the flap. Moaning about the crowded pub and the music not being played in the traditional way he likes, he gets out of his wet clothes and into his sleeping-bag.

We lay side by side, neither of us speaking. Sean turns away from me and I put my back to his. His snores and the separate sleeping-bags create a barrier; the laughter of campers being blown to their beds tells me it doesn't have to be this way.

The sky is grey but at least the rain has stopped and we are able to decamp.

We look at two gable ends precariously supporting the remains of a roof; shattered slates litter the ground around what is left of a traditional Irish cottage.

'That can't be the house,' I say. 'The estate agent said it needs work, not that it needs rebuilding. I'll go and enquire at the takeaway.'

I go back to where we'd joined early risers queuing for bacon rolls.

'Yes,' says the man serving, 'it's Raheen's Cottage... Yes, it is for sale.'

Raheen's Cottage is the first of many 'cottage kits' (as Sean calls them). Sometimes the estate agent's details are a piece of fiction creating an image of what a cottage hunter might want, rather than what's on offer.

I point to a dilapidated building. 'Is this O'Brien's house?' I ask three boys in short grey trousers; they nod in agreement. Showing them the house details, I point to the wording. 'Look here, it says it has a lake view. Can you see a lake from here? Is there a lake anywhere near here?'

'Creedy's Lake is about ten miles away,' says one boy.

'But can you see it from here?' I persist.

Looking warily at me, he shakes his head.

'So, these details are incorrect. In other words, they're lying!' I screw up the paper, shoving it into my pocket as I stride towards Sean who's retreating in the car.

Our search in Clare and Galway has been disappointing, so we continue northwards and arrive at the beautiful island-spattered bay of Clew in County Mayo. Inspired by the breath-taking views, but unable to afford the house prices, we continued to drive further into Mayo. Houses are now fewer, and the land has flattened out into what seems to be a never-ending bog. We're out of food. We drive on, looking for a shop, a campsite or even a hotel until, forced by oncoming darkness, we pull off the road onto a piece of rough ground.

Thankfully, we bought a torch in Galway, so we're able to erect the tent and find enough scraps of wood to light a fire. Sean opens our one bottle of wine and fills two glasses. We've only just sat down by the fire when we're suddenly startled by headlights illuminating our camp. A car pulls in and parks next to ours. A man of about forty, wearing Wellingtons and a flat cap, gets out of the car. 'Jesus, what the feck are you doing here?' he asks.

Standing up, I explain. 'We're camping. We couldn't find anywhere else to put a tent.'

He peers at Sean, who is sat on the ground with a sleeping-bag around his shoulders, looking more like a North American Indian than an English tourist. 'This is a rubbish tip,' explains the man. 'I saw the fire from my window.'

Falling into the role of hostess, I pick up the bottle of red wine. 'Would you like a drink? Though you'll have to have a mug; we only brought two glasses.'

'What is it?' he asks.

'Red wine; Merlot, I think,' I say, looking at the label.

'Wine!' he exclaims, pulling a disgusted face. 'I wouldn't touch the stuff.'

'Have you ever tried it?' I ask.

'No, I drink Guinness and whiskey.'

'Is there a pub near here?' asks Sean from the fireside.

'No. There's a general store about a mile down the road. We drink in there.'

Do they sell wine?' persists Sean.

Our visitor expresses his revulsion with a loud, 'Jesus, no! They only sell whiskey and Guinness.'

Our guest doesn't stay long. When he drives away, both Sean and I agree, Mayo is not for us!

There's one last house on our list. It's on the west coast of Clare, not far from a small town called Miltown. We made a decision not to view the house – we'd gone to Miltown a few years ago to buy petrol and thought it a depressing little place. Mind, at the time, we were both in a bad mood. I was angry with Sean as the previous night he'd got very drunk. Sean was annoyed because the landlord had asked him to leave. This may have given us an unfair view of the place, but with only a couple of days left I don't want to go on another wild goose chase.

Sean insists we view the house. Reluctantly, I give in and we head back in the direction of West Clare.

Miltown's church steeple comes into view a mile before we reach the town. We see a sign pointing to Miltown; it leads us past a line of stone-built cabins onto a road wide enough to suggest that Miltown is, or had once been, a market town. We park outside the church; the towering austere building reminds me just how important religion is in Ireland.

We take a slow walk. There's a bank, two small supermarkets, a shabby hotel, a baker's, an estate agent, two gift shops, and eight pubs. A line of traffic waits patiently behind a lorry delivering Guinness. Tractors and cars are amicably double and treble parked on either side of the road.

I was mistaken about the town; the people seem friendly, the shops are busy, there's a nice atmosphere about the place. The weather helps; the wind has taken a rest and the sun is shining.

When we leave the town and drive a couple of miles up a fuchsia-edged road, I begin to feel that somehow we might be on the right track.

We park the car. I stand at the top of Lashen Hill, look down at Miltown and across to the never-ending sea sparkling in the distance. I cast my eye around me. As well as a detached bungalow opposite a lane and another one further down the hill, there's a small whitewashed cottage. We look at the photograph and reread the estate agent's details. My voice rises in exasperation when I say, 'That can't be it. Where are the outbuildings? It's another wild goose chase! Let's go.' I'm about to march to the car when I spot two chimneys on a slate roof and what looks like slabs of stone on another building. I point across a bramble-covered stone wall and a field spiked with rushes and say, 'Look, there it is!'

We follow the nearby lane into what looks like an abandoned farmyard. Rushes and weeds have colonised the muddy puddles and cracked concrete. Brambles have spread their way across the yard, capturing broken buckets, discarded tools and rusting farm equipment.

A scruffy black and white collie appears, moves slowly towards us with its head down and a faint wag of its tail.

We stroke the dog's matted coat and gaze at the house. Broken gutters have deposited streaks of green algae on the dirt grey walls; curtains of cobwebs conceal what's behind the windows; moss covered sandbags against a weatherworn door suggest nobody's been in the house for a very long time.

We turn to the outbuilding; three battered doors hang on their hinges. We open one and, followed by the dog, walk into a room full of wet peat. Another two rooms have chains attached to the walls, suggesting they'd once housed animals.

We go back outside, move a wooden pallet and make our way to the back of the house. A small field is occupied by a cow and her calf; the calf, wary, moves close to her grazing mother. We look across to where the land falls away into a patchwork of fields stitched with dry stone walls, to where it stretches on and on to the horizon of hazy hills.

A small group of scraggy, wind-torn pines stand in an untidy group on the western edge of the field. We give the cow a wide berth as we walk towards them. We climb over a fallen tree, make our way through the pines to a bird's-eye view of the sea and the distant Kerry mountains. The air is full of birdsong and I stand entranced by the sights and sounds around me. I'm not surprised to hear Sean say, 'The estate agent said we can pick the keys up from the bungalow at the top of the lane.'

At the door of the neat bungalow, a young woman hands us the key. She tells us the house hasn't been lived in since her uncle died two years ago and to excuse the mess.

We go back to the house. Sean gives the door a hefty shove and we step over the sandbags into a large, lofty room. The first thing that hits me is the cold. None of the light bulbs are working, though there is electricity. An orange glow from a flickering electric candle takes our attention to a framed picture. I squint in the half dark at a print of the Virgin and Child. Sean peers over my shoulder. 'It's the Virgin Mary,' I tell him.

'Why's there pigeons in the corner?'

'They're not pigeons, you dope! They're angels.'

We burst out laughing and I know Sean loves this house as much as I do; that despite the damp, the stained flagstones, the cracked Belfast sink, the mould on the doors, we want it to be ours.

We climb a small flight of stairs, ducking our heads as we go into an attic room. I touch the back of roof slates warmed by the sun; a small window in the gable gives a hazy view of grazing cattle. 'This will be our bedroom,' I tell myself. 'We will be happy here.'

We go downstairs and wander through the remaining three rooms. The amount of work piles up – rusting fireplaces, rotting floorboards, rewiring, no heating, no bathroom or lavatory. But no matter, because when Sean says, 'What do you think?'

I say 'Yes!'

We leave the house. The dog is waiting at the door. He follows us up the lane to the bungalow.

Sean gives the young woman the key, saying, 'We want to make an offer.'

'Well, that's grand,' she says. 'My name's Mary.' She picks up the young child who clings to her skirt. 'This here is Liam.'

We introduce ourselves. 'Who does the black and white collie belong to?' I ask.

'He was my uncle's.'

'What's its name?'

'He's called Blackie. Would you like to come in for a cup of tea?'

I look at Sean.

'We'd better not,' he says. 'We need to get going.'

'We're in a bit of a rush,' I tell her, 'but we'll be in touch. We'll ring the agent as soon as we get home.'

Blackie is standing by Mary's gate. He follows us across the road. Sean and I look down at what will be our house – all is quiet in the little homestead. Sean gets into the car. I stroke Blackie's head, promising to get rid of the wads of knots in his fur, telling him that we'll be back.

CHAPTER 2

A pewter sky, the cold wind lifting the dust from the ground, threatens the Easter weekend. Without the sun and the holidaymakers, Miltown shows its true colours, an out-of-the-way, rundown town with a handful of people dressed in coats and hats traipsing in and out of the few shops that are open.

We book a room for the night in a pub called Clancy. With its flowery wallpaper, brown shag-pile carpet and pink candlewick bedspread, the room wouldn't be out of place in a museum.

Leaving our cases behind, we drive out of town onto the Lisheen road. I look out of the window; the fuchsia flowers are long gone, leaving the hedgerows as thin and as featureless as the empty fields. By the time we park outside Mary's bungalow I'm beginning to wonder if we've done the right thing, if we'd made a now-or-never decision without thinking it through properly. Whether we like it or not, there's no going back – the house is ours now!

The warmth in Mary's kitchen wraps like a blanket. Mary's husband is with her. Tom, a fresh-faced man of about forty, finishes putting on his thick grey overcoat then shakes our hand with a firm grip, saying, 'Welcome, it's a shame about the weather; it's a miserable day for the time of year.'

'We're only here for a few days,' says Sean. 'Once the contract was signed I wanted to get over here and assess what needs doing.'

'Well, if there's anything I can help you with just ask,' offers Tom. 'But I must get going; the cattle need feeding.' He raises his hand. 'Bye for now.'

A girl of about eight puts her head around the kitchen door. 'Come and say hello to Sean and Anna,' Mary tells her.

The girl comes shyly into the room.

'This is our daughter, Clare. Is Liam still asleep?' Mary asks her.

Clare nods her head.

'Well, go and wake him; Gran will think we're not coming.'

Clare runs from the room. Mary turns to us, asking, 'Where are you staying?'

'We've booked into a pub called Clancy,' I tell her.

'You'll get a good meal there. I'd offer you a meal myself, but we're taking Tom's mam to mass.'

'We must go too,' says Sean. 'We want to take a look at the house before it gets dark.'

'Tom's put new light bulbs in,' says Mary, going to a cupboard. She takes out a key and gives it to Sean. 'If there's anything we can do, don't be afraid to ask.'

We leave the comfort of Mary's kitchen and drive down the lane to the house. Blackie appears from nowhere, greeting us with his head down and his tail wagging. I rub his neck; the wads of fur are thicker than ever. 'Next time we come I'll bring a pair of scissors,' I tell him.

Sean has opened the door and gone into the house. I step over the sandbags and join him.

The first thing that hits me is the smell of damp; the light-bulb gives enough light to see the large wet patches on the chimney breast. The four downstairs rooms are as we remember them; it is the grey day that has cast a measure of doubt. I remind myself that this is the house we fell in love with; the only difference between then and now is the weather. We go into the attic room and the roof slates rattle a draughty welcome.

Mary was right, the boiled bacon and carrots they serve in Clancy is generous and delicious. The young man behind the bar notices Sean's fiddle case and tells us about a music session being held tonight in a nearby pub.

Freil's pub is busy. People of all ages are sat on long wooden benches. They smile a welcome and shift along to make room for us. In the middle of the room, four men and a woman are sat around a Formica top table, their instruments – bodhran, flute, concertina, guitar and whistle – are on the table in front of them.

The woman spots Sean's fiddle case and beckons him over. He comes back and tells me he's going to play a few tunes. One of the musicians gets a chair from behind the bar; another calls the barman to 'Bring the man a pint.'

I watch them introduce themselves. They pick up their instruments; someone calls 'quiet' and the music starts.

I don't take my eyes from Sean – the barman replenishing his glass; Sean downing his drink whenever he sees the barman coming.

Sean's eyes are beginning to glaze, his fiddle is now in its case on the floor. He tries to roll a cigarette and the tobacco falls from the loosely rolled paper. He tries again and manages to put a twisted roll up between his lips; a few attempts are made to strike a match. Eventually he manages to light the cigarette then sits back into his chair.

I know him so well; one or two more drinks and he'll be spilling them or, worse still, he'll be on the floor, shaming me in front of all these people.

The musicians continue playing. Ignoring Sean, they talk to each other between tunes. I'm praying they'll stop serving soon. I've been told that, as it's Good Friday tomorrow, they're not allowed to sell alcohol after midnight. At 12.04 a.m., Sean swallows his last dreg. There's no problem getting him to leave now the bar is closed!

The temperature has dropped. I put my collar up and we make our way to Clancy's. The bar is in darkness; it looks as though it had closed long before the midnight curfew. I take the key from my purse, unlock the door and we go into the dimly light corridor. An elderly man stands up from a chair, glares at us and in a loud aggressive voice asks, 'Where have you been!'

Rather taken aback, I say, 'Freil's. Why?'

'I've been waiting for you. I'm the landlord. It's Good Friday. You can't stay here.'

'We're booked in.'

'I'm going to unbook you. I'm not allowed to open on Good Friday.'

I hear Sean say, 'Anna, let's get our things.'

Ignoring him, I tell the landlord, 'Our cases are here. A man behind the bar took the booking.'

'He's my son. He shouldn't have.'

Sean grabs my shoulder. 'Come on,' he says. 'Let's get our cases and get out of here.'

'But...'

He pushes me towards the stairs and, reluctantly, I follow.

We gather our things together. The landlord opens the door as soon as he sees us coming. Sean picks up his fiddle-case and we step out into the cold.

Wondering what to do, hoping for an answer, I look around me. Sean gets into the car, starts the engine and tells me to 'Get in' – he has sobered up remarkably quickly. Assuring myself it's only a three-mile drive to the house and nobody will be out on a night like this and promising myself I'll pass my next driving-test, I get into the car.

The night is black, the road deserted. The only sign of life is Blackie when he comes to greet us. The house is ominous and uninviting; we don't even discuss where we're going to sleep. We search through our suitcases and put on as many clothes as we can manage. Sean puts the back seats down; we climb into the car and wriggle into our sleeping-bags – brought in case of an emergency. It's surprisingly comfortable and the next thing I know it is morning.

The wind is bitterly cold and unrelenting. There's enough peat in the outbuilding to be extravagant and soon a fire is burning in every room.

We explore the house, looking in every nook and cranny, making plans, wondering if we should keep the flagstones – they look as though they belong in a cowshed. I tell Sean I want the kitchen to be the heart of the house, an Aga to cook on, a big wooden table, warmth and colour and light.

We drive into town to buy food. I'm excited about the future, feel a sense of relief knowing it is Good Friday and nobody will be selling alcohol.

Disappointment falls like a brick when I see the supermarket shelves. As well as food, cleaning materials and the essentials, Sean buys three bottles of wine and six cans of lager.

As soon as we arrive back at the house, Sean drags an old vinyl sofa from the outbuilding, takes it into the back room and puts it in front of the fire.

I busy myself at the Belfast sink, filling an old bucket with water and heating it on the fire, washing the insides of cupboards, finding places to put the food, swiping at cobwebs, washing the windows, sweeping the floor.

The hours tick by. Sean doesn't hear me open the door to the back room, doesn't know I'm watching him swigging wine from the bottle, the ash falling from his cigarette, the two empty bottles in front of the dying fire, the three empty lager cans that have rolled across the floor. I close the door, put my coat on and go outside. Blackie joins me and together we walk up the lane.

The fight against the wind takes my mind away from Sean. I concentrate on what's around me: the dog at my side, the empty road, the quiet fields, the smoke drifting from cottage chimneys.

I think about this morning. Sean is never far from my thoughts. We are both so enthusiastic. By putting his time and energies into the house Sean won't feel the need to drink. The musicians he played with last night were welcoming – the sort of people I would love him to mix with. We're three miles from any pub; Sean won't risk losing his licence again. If we lived here we would be on a tighter budget and he wouldn't be able to afford to drink. Sean needs to be away from the city. Here, in the peace of the country, the two of us working on the house will bring us back together.

I turn around; the wind behind me pushing me onwards.

Sean is lying on the floor asleep. He doesn't wake when I put more peat on the fire and, for a minute, I watch the wisps of smoke curling up into the chimney. A knock on the door calls me.

Tom and his daughter, Clare, are waiting outside. 'We noticed the car,' says Tom. 'We wondered if there's anything you need? We've a couple of Calor gas heaters you can use.'

'Thank you, we've lit all the fires; we're quite warm.'

I don't invite them in; I'd rather they didn't see Sean.

'I noticed the car when I came to feed the cattle; you were here early.'

'We came last night. Being Good Friday, the landlord's son shouldn't have booked us in and we were asked to leave.

Tom's waiting to be invited in. I hear a noise. Sean's slurred voice is saying, 'There's a hell of a draught. Who are you talking to?'

'Tom,' I say.

'What's he doing out there? Invite him in! Get the man a glass. Pour him a drink.'

Tom and Clare follow me into the house and into the back room.

Sean has lifted himself up from the floor and collapsed onto the sofa. Tom, steady and clear-eyed, and his rosy-cheeked daughter stare at Sean as he attempts to sit up. He falls back, a grin on his flushed face and I wish with all my heart they hadn't come into the house.

CHAPTER 3

Blissful Sunday morning! I spread my arms and breathe in the luxury of the spacious bed, anticipating the freedom of the long day before me.

In the thirty-two years Sean and I have been together, we have seldom been apart. The first time I saw him he was walking along a busy shopping street towards me. I was so struck by his grace and beauty that I'd quickly stepped inside a shop doorway. As he came closer, I saw that beneath the dark hair were the biggest, greenest eyes I had ever seen. I turned to watch him walk away. The energy in his step as he disappeared into the bustling street remained an image in my mind.

A couple of weeks later, I went into a pub with some friends, and there he was playing his fiddle. I sat entranced, not only by his looks, but by his music as well. When he finished playing he came to my table and we started talking. He offered to buy me a drink; by the end of the evening we had made a date.

It became apparent quite soon that he had a drink problem, but I thought a home and my love was all he needed, so he moved out of his grotty bed-sit, I left my mother's house, and we rented a flat. Twelve months later I was pregnant with Alice and we married.

Sean and David left for Ireland yesterday. As well as being a good friend, David had been Sean's employer. As soon as David turned fifty he retired. He'd made a lot of money from his building firm, so he bought a heap of houses, filled them with tenants and is now living on the proceeds, enjoying life with time on his hands. It was David's redundancy payment to Sean that enabled us to buy the house in Ireland. Having

David with him will encourage Sean to get on with the job of making the house habitable; they both have an equal admiration for each other's building skills and enjoy the banter when they're together. Sean jokes that David is his mentor, as well as his tormentor, but they respect each other and rarely disagree, which was why David never complained about the Mondays Sean arrived late for work, the days he failed to turn up because of hangovers. Just docking Sean's pay suited them both.

Attractive, prosperous and single, David usually has one, sometimes two women in tow! A few have arrived at our dinner table to be vetted and approved by Sean and I. Most of them are never seen again. We've given up hope of him meeting the right girl; we're not even sure he's knows what he's looking for.

I get out of bed and pad barefoot to the kitchen. I love this house. We bought it twenty years ago, about the same time that Sean started working for David. The large Victorian semi was a bargain price because of the amount of work needing doing to it – leaking roof, old wiring, no central heating, outdated kitchen. It took us years to restore it. The spacious rooms, sanded floorboards, the marble fireplaces and ornate cornices gave us a house to be proud of. Now the girls have left home we don't need so many rooms, but today I'm relishing the peace as much as the space. Not having Sean here means I'll go to bed on Sunday night knowing he won't be bringing half the pub back. Not having to listen to music being played all hours means I shall go to work on Monday morning feeling refreshed, not seething with anger because Sean is fast asleep at home.

Liz, Sue and Vicky were here last evening. They arrived at 7 o'clock bearing chocolates and wine. Not worrying about

Sean being bored with our chatter, or me counting each drink he drank, made our time together relaxing, enjoyable.

This morning I feel like a teenager. I've done nothing but slop around in my dressing gown, listening to The Beatles and reading. The newspapers and Sunday supplements are spread across the coffee table together with my empty mug. Alice, little Ella and Kate will be here in an hour. I did manage to shove a joint into the oven, and the smell of roasting lamb is now beginning to drift from the kitchen.

The three of us are sat by the open patio door. Ella is playing in the garden. I've told them I'll wash the dishes when they've gone. We watch Ella run across the lawn to the sunny spot where Lily is sleeping. Lily, suddenly awake, dashes into the apple tree, glares at Ella from a safe place amongst the blossom.

'How long will Dad be gone?' asks Kate.

'It's hard to say. I'll be with him in three weeks. The plan was we'd come back together but it wouldn't surprise me if he stays on. There's so much to do: a septic tank to put in, and he needs to build an extension for the bathroom.'

'How long's David staying?'

'A couple of weeks. Longer if I had my way. David won't want to go to the pub; you know what he's like, he'll carry on until the job's finished.'

Alice stands up. 'Ella, get down off that tree. Leave Lily alone.' She sits back down, saying, 'She's such a tomboy; clothes don't last a minute. I'm sure she'll love Ireland – the space and the sea. Adam and I are looking forward to coming over.'

"So am I,' says Kate. 'I want to know when to book my holidays.'

'Well, it may not be this year. Not unless you're happy to go without a shower and willing to dig a hole outside when you need to go to the loo.'

Alice and Kate look at each other. 'Um, perhaps not then; maybe we'll wait.'

'Ella! I told you,' shouts Alice, standing up again. 'Come down!'

Three weeks have flown by; before I know it, I'm at the airport saying goodbye to Kate. 'I promise I'll write,' I say. 'Tell Alice I'll let you both know how it's all going.'

Dear Girls

I'm sorry this letter has taken so long, but time has just flown by.

Your dad is looking so well; this lifestyle certainly does suit him. We start work soon after breakfast: dad on the house and, depending on the weather, with me accompanied by my good friend Blackie, clearing the field from grass by the old-fashioned method of digging. Some days, we've become so engrossed in what we're doing it's late afternoon before we realise that we haven't had lunch!

By Irish standards, the weather has been good. We had a couple of days when the rain fell almost vertically, but for the rest of the time we've had a mixture of soft (Irish for light, almost misty) rain, cloudy and sunny days and, of course, wind in its various degrees.

We've become real home birds. Other than shopping for food and building materials, we go out one evening a week to a music session in a pub called Michael's. I drive us home. Thank goodness I passed my test. We usually pick up a few late-night stragglers on the way. If they live near, I drop them at their house, otherwise they make their own way home.

Life in the sticks is without the boundaries of city life. Twice I've been shocked to find a strange man in the house; both times Sean was out buying building materials. I nearly jumped out of my skin when a man walked into the sitting room and introduced himself as Joe the postie. Another time I came into the house and met a very elderly gentleman coming down the stairs. He told me he was the meter reader. He was writing the numbers in a little notebook with a pencil he kept behind his ear.

I didn't see David – he left the day before I arrived. He and Sean had certainly worked hard. All the floors had been taken up and a damp-proof membrane put over the whole area. The bedrooms and sitting room now have new floor boards and the flagstones have been replaced with quarry tiles. They look fantastic. The flagstones will become the patio. Sean is now re-wiring. The next step will be to install a septic tank and build an extension for a bathroom.

We've already bought something for the garden, a Rowan tree for its berries; I want to encourage the birds. I have many plans for the garden. I'm going to create a vegetable patch and a herb and flower garden, despite being told by the neighbours that 'you won't be able to garden here – the wind's too fierce.' I think they're wrong. I'll plant wind breaks and use tough, salt resistant plants.

Mary called in a couple of days ago. She gave us thirty punts. She said it is the lucky penny, an old custom where the seller gives the buyer a small sum of money which brings them both good luck.

I've met an elderly woman called Bridie who lives in a nearby bungalow. She likes going for walks and I often meet her on my evening strolls. She sometimes invites me in and, over a cup of tea, she tells me about life in and around Miltown when she was growing up. She must be well into her seventies. She lived here when there was no electricity and water had to be drawn from a well. The only person to own a car was the doctor. Others, if they were lucky, travelled by horse and cart, bicycle, or a good pair of shoes!

One more week and I'll be home, and back to work. I was hoping to start a watercolour painting; the scenery *really inspires me, but there hasn't been the time. Still, it will be here when I come back!*

I don't think your dad will be returning with me. I understand how he feels. One evening I was standing at the bottom of our field, looking down and across the panoramic view. I felt as though I was on top of the world. Birdsong was all around. Martins were swooping through the air. I looked back towards the cottage where wisps of smoke rose from the chimney against an evening sky, red from the setting sun. Living in such surroundings must bring peace and contentment to anyone.

I'm looking forward to seeing you all soon. Give a hug and a kiss to Ella from me; tell her I'm looking forward to taking her to the park.

Lots of love, Mum x

P.S. Kate, Dad says give up that dreadful classical stuff and learn a few Irish jigs and reels. He wants to play a few tunes with you. He sends his love to you all.

I've been back a whole month. Sean arrived three days ago and hasn't stopped talking about Ireland since. He was there for nearly nine weeks; it was only loneliness that drove him home.

He is so enthusiastic about Ireland and the house. 'Look, Anna, this place is far too big for us. You complain yourself about the expense of running it, about the amount of traffic on the road and not being able to park outside your own front door. You don't like the city. You've said so time and time again. You said you want a smaller house and a larger garden. Now you have one. You can't garden it from here!'

'But what about the girls? What about Ella?'

'What about them? They have their own lives to live. They'll visit. They'll see what a better life we're having. They might even be tempted to move over themselves. Adam's a plumber; he can always get work. Kate's free to go wherever she wants; nurses are always in short supply. As for Ella, they'll see it's a far better place to bring up a kid.'

I had to agree. There'd been a spate of crime in our area. The car had been broken into, the house burgled twice, and I'd had my handbag snatched when walking through the park.

'Look, Anna, there's nothing to keep us here. You've said yourself Social Services are making cuts and you might lose your job. This house is worth five times what we paid for it, and the mortgage is paid. If we sell this house we'll have more than enough to buy two smaller ones to let, which will give us an income.'

It's true – all he says is true – but he doesn't realise that sometimes I'm a hair's breadth away from leaving him. He seems to be oblivious to how difficult I find life with him, especially since the girls left. More and more I find myself on the verge of walking out; always something holds me back – a hope that growing older together will bring us closer. Perhaps that hope lays in Ireland.

Today I agreed to put the house on the market.

CHAPTER 4

It all happened so fast, though it came as no surprise when our lovely house sold quickly. Just three weeks after putting it on the market, we were offered the asking price. Then the rush came to find two properties suitable to put tenants in. We were cash buyers and had the pick of the market; it wasn't long before we found what we were looking for.

We moved into this small Victorian terraced house just before Christmas. Both houses needed a few jobs done before looking for tenants. Sean replaced a couple of tiles on the roof but there's still a bit of plumbing, plastering and decorating to do.

We've acquired a lot of things over the years – far too much to fit into the house in Ireland. The girls picked over what was surplus to our needs. The bits they didn't want are back in the charity and junk shops where we found them.

David's help made the move so much easier. I thought saying goodbye to our beautiful house was going to be difficult but, as always, David's company lightened the mood. The repartee between him and Sean is so funny; I was soon laughing.

Lily arrived with the last load. She was frantic; clawing at the door of her pet carrier, howling wide eyed with terror. Sean carried her up the stairs and shut her in the small bedroom crammed with furniture and bulging boxes to try and calm her.

David and I went outside into the narrow back garden. We were discussing what could be done to smarten it up when a voice with a strong Bristolian accent called, 'Hello, you're lucky the rain stayed off.'

A buxom woman of about forty, with bleached blonde hair and wearing fluorescent orange lipstick, suddenly blossomed amongst next-door's plastic flowers. Smiling at us from across the low brick wall, she introduced herself as Blodwyn. 'That's not my real name,' she said. 'My real name's Audrey; they call me Blodwyn cos I was born in Wales.' She asked if we wanted a cup of tea. A few minutes later she was passing three steaming mugs across the wall, saying, 'I'm glad you're not black; a family of them moved into number two. Before you know it, they'll be taking over!'

She seemed to think David was my husband. 'No,' I said, 'I'm married to Sean; he's upstairs trying to calm the cat.' She was disappointed when I told her we were putting tenants in the house. I assured her we would ask for references and that they would be nice people. I didn't promise they would be white.

Blodwyn came as a bit of a shock. It took us a good two years after Jean moved in to be on friendly enough terms to ask her to feed the cat. We'd been living in a neighbourhood where social contact was kept to the minimum 'good morning' and 'evening'. Any hint of racism amongst our white middle-class neighbours would be treated with horror. Their children, protected against such things, were kept off the street – unlike Wellington Road, where at weekends it becomes a kid's playground, with balls flying, and parked cars become hiding places.

Alice and Adam live a ten-minute walk from here. Earlier this evening, I collected Ella from the house, and took her to the carnival in the city centre. Everyone's excited about the new Millennium. Massive amounts of money have been spent on the celebrations. The costumes were fabulous, the lights superb and there's going to be a huge firework display at midnight. People are welcoming the coming year with such optimism, but will the world become a better place when the hand passes midnight and the numbers change? I wish it were that easy.

When I took Ella home, a group of Alice and Adam's friends were beginning to arrive. Alice invited me to join them, but I felt the need to be on my own.

This is the first time I've been alone in the house. Lily is avoiding me, hiding away in some dark place in the small bedroom. Sean is the other side of town with his mates, playing in the Millennium.

I feel strangely detached in this tiny sitting-room, as though I'm on a remote railway platform waiting for a train to take me on an epic journey to a place I do not know. From a back garden a few doors away comes the sound of laughter. Rockets explode, bringing cries of appreciation, signalling the midnight hour. It's another world to the one I'm in. Despite the noise, the peace in this room remains undisturbed. A fortress of silence stood between me and the celebrations.

CHAPTER 5

The silver basket containing the elegant bouquet of narcissus and iris looks incongruous amongst Sean's tools on the table, the flowers' delicate beauty quite out of place in the chaotic kitchen, full of plumbing and building materials.

We were curious when the van drove down the lane. We thought a mistake had been made when the burly driver handed me the flowers. 'I had a helluva job finding you,' he said. 'I eventually rang on someone's bell and they told me an English couple had moved here.'

I signed for the flowers then watched the van rattle its way back up the lane.

Tucked amongst the yellow and mauve spring bouquet is a little silver and pink card that reads:

To Mum and Dad,
Best wishes and good luck in your new home.
Love from Kate and Alice.

The flowers are from a shop near where we used to live. They were slightly jaded from their long journey, but now, after a cool drink, they look fresh and bright.

They bring wistful thoughts. If only Alice, Kate and Ella had burst out of the van, bright and sunny as sunflowers, streamers flying as they shout, 'Surprise, Surprise!'

The flowers are lovely, but small recompense for... for what? I ask myself. A dream?

The flowers arrived two days ago. Exactly three weeks after David left. He only stayed one night; the van we hired to move us had to be returned the following day. It was with a touch of sadness that I watched him drive away. Suddenly, I'd felt very alone which, of course, is ridiculous. Sean and I chose to live here. We were looking forward to a bright and happy future.

I take my eyes from the flowers to look at Lily. She has put her nose outside the door and is sniffing the air; her tail disappears as she slinks out of the house. I move to the door and watch her inch her way against the wall. Blackie has noticed her; he sits up with ears pricked, puts his head between his paws, stares at her as she creeps across the yard and vanishes under my car.

Yes, I now have my very own car – a blue Cinquecento that looks conspicuously clean parked on the broken concrete next to Sean's old grey Ford.

I took my car out for a drive yesterday; I wasn't sure who was in control, the car or me. I feel as though some strange little alien has suddenly landed in the yard, and I have to get to know it very cautiously. Still, I don't have to wait for Sean to give me a lift.

Wondering if Sean needs anything from the hardware shop, I follow the sound of an Irish jig, and the intermittent noise of a drill. Sean is on the floor connecting our future bathroom to the newly installed septic tank.

'I'm going into town. Do you need anything?' I ask.

He sits up and turns the tape-recorder down. 'Yes, a couple of bottles of wine and a pack of Special Brew and some tobacco.'

'I thought we were going out? What about the session?'

'I'm giving it a miss. They're a miserable lot.'

'That's a shame. Why? You enjoy playing in pubs. It's a good way to meet people.'

He turns the music up, picks up his drill, saying, 'I don't like the way they play. They take the life out of the music. I'd rather have a few drinks at home and listen to my tapes.'

I drive into town, thinking about the session. It's not so much the playing Sean doesn't like, but the fact they stay sober. I'd hoped some of their qualities might rub off on Sean. I fear that's not going to be. I've noticed a change in their attitude towards him; they don't make space when they see him coming. He's ignored – barely tolerated.

Not having the confidence to join the double and treble parked cars, I drive further along the road, find a nice large space and walk to the supermarket.

When it comes to shopping for food, I'm never spoilt for choice – Kelly's sell only the basics. Nor do they waste time on displays – potatoes, carrots, cabbages and onions are left on the floor in the sacks they arrive in. Today, the salad section consists of two soft tomatoes, three collapsed lettuces and one yellow cucumber. There are two types of cheese – white and orange. Bread is ready-wrapped, brown or white, thick, medium or thinly sliced.

The drink section is always well stocked. I read the labels on the wine bottles before picking up two bottles with the lowest alcohol content and a pack of Special Brew, reluctantly putting them in my trolley.

As soon as we finish eating, Sean takes the bag of drinks into the back room. I clear away the dishes, put on my coat and go outside. Blackie follows me to the top of the lane. I see Bridie, a mere speck in the distance. She's surprised when I appear at her side – I'd told her that Sean and I were going to the session – mumbling a lie about Sean having to work on the house.

Bridie slows her pace to mine, telling me about her life in Ireland when she was a child – collecting water from the well, helping on the farm, the long walk to school, taking the teacher's horse to the stable. Only the doctor had a car.

All too soon, she stops, turns towards the way we came and I've no other choice than to follow her. We stand in front of her bungalow. I hover at her gate, waiting to be invited in.

We sit in her sitting-room drinking tea. She describes the work she did in the ammunition factory in London and her training and job as a typist, when the war was over. She retired five years ago when she bought the bungalow.

Other than family, Bridie doesn't mention anyone close in her life. Her brother John and his wife live nearby; she doesn't see them often as they're busy with the farm and countless grandchildren. I'm sure, like me, she's lonely. After three cups of tea, and not wanting to outstay my welcome, I reluctantly say goodnight.

Blackie wags his tail when he sees me – his devotion doing little to lift me when he follows me home. Stepping into the house, I creep through the kitchen and up the stairs. Sean's taped music follows me from the back room. I close the bedroom door, getting into bed as I listen to the music, waiting for it to pass into silence.

Tom's tractor, trundling to the milking shed, wakes me just before 7.00 a.m. I slowly get dressed, then go downstairs. Sean is asleep with Lily on the sofa. As soon as she sees me, she jumps to the floor. I quickly go to the kitchen, feed her, and make myself a sandwich.

Blackie follows me to the outbuilding, watches me fill the wheelbarrow with garden tools. I go to the plot I'm digging – lettuces and radishes are beginning to push their way through the soil. The sound of distant barking makes Blackie's ears prick. The barking gets louder and Blackie runs from the garden to the front of the house, ready – as Sean so aptly puts it – to join the dog relay. I leave what I'm doing; within a minute, Joe's post van hurtles down the lane. Blackie runs towards it, barking loudly, skilfully missing the van's wheels. Joe pulls up beside me and hands me a letter. Blackie pants with excitement. The van shoots back up the lane. Blackie chases after it to where Tom's dog Goldie is waiting to run the next leg.

The address on the envelope is written in Kate's full, rounded handwriting. I open it.

Dear Mum and Dad,

I hope you're both well. This is just a short note to let you know I'M IN LOVE! I met Sam a few weeks ago when he came to work on my ward as charge nurse. He's handsome, fantastic and just wonderful. I know you'll like him and I want you to meet him. We've been able to book off the first week in June. Is it okay to come over?

Give us a ring, as soon as possible. (When is your phone going to be connected?) Can't wait to see you and for you to meet Sam!

Loads of love,

Kate xxxx

To my knowledge, Kate has never been in love. Boyfriends were never in short supply, but they came and went. Kate is twenty-six years old and seems to enjoy being single. She shares a house with other nurses, fills her time with work and a hectic social life.

June is less than eight weeks away. The thought of her visit sends a rush of excitement. I curse not having a phone. We've been waiting a month to be connected. When I get in touch with the telephone company, they say, 'In a few days.' When I told Tom about it, he said, 'a few days means they don't want to disappoint you.' I don't understand "Irish logic".

I rush into the house, shake Sean awake, and I give him the letter.

'I'll read it later,' he moans, putting his face to the cushion.

'I'm going into town to phone her now,' I say. Without waiting for a reply, I grab my car keys.

Sean tells me the house isn't ready for visitors. I look at him in amazement. 'Kate's not a visitor! She's our daughter. I told her we can't wait to see her and to book the flights. She's coming whether you like it or not!'

I'm upset by Sean's attitude. I thought digging and pulling up brambles would curb my temper, but I've been here for over an hour and I'm still seething. Leaving the tools in the wheelbarrow, I go into the house, find my camera and drive to Bridie's.

I was hoping a walk on the beach with Bridie would calm me, but it hasn't. I keep asking myself why Sean doesn't want Kate to come. Why he's become reclusive. Why he's drinking more than ever.

I take photographs of waves roaring their way to land, crashing foam and spray onto the deserted beach. I'll throw colours onto a canvas, taking ominous greys and indigo blues to create a threatening sky and I won't stop until I feel its roar.

I say goodbye to Bridie and drive home. As I step out of the car, Sean appears, saying, 'I've just made tea, do you want one?' I nod my head. I've lived through these binges so often I know the course of events.

I walk to the back of the house, sit on the bench with my back against the wall and the sun on my face. Sean hands me a cup of tea, sits beside me, saying, 'I could never move back to Bristol; it's the space I love. Look at it! Miles of emptiness! Who needs people!' A shutter falls across my mind. We sit for a while saying nothing. Sean picks up the empty cups and goes inside. Soon, the sad strains of a slow and beautiful air drift from the house.

I stroke the dog, listening to the music. It could all be so perfect – a house in the country, time to pursue my love of landscape painting and a garden large enough to grow our own food. Trouble is, there's one bad chord in this idyll and, for the life of me, I can't see how to get rid of it.

CHAPTER 6

For the past couple of months, people have been talking about nothing but Miltown's annual Irish music festival. At long last it's about to happen. The week-long festival starts tomorrow. Traditional Irish music, in its many forms – instrumental, song and dance – will be taught in every available space, be it the community centre, pubs, hotels or someone's sitting room. Accommodation is in such short supply; B&B vacancy signs are taken down almost as soon as they appear. Hundreds enrol for classes; at least three times as many come for the "Craic".

The coming festival has certainly enlivened the town. Everyone's been busy; front doors are bright with new paint, flowers bloom on window ledges. Shops that had been closed since we moved here are open, their windows cleared of cobwebs and dressed with displays of musical instruments, books, CDs, tapes and old records. Others have menus Blu-Tacked to their newly polished windows, the spotless rooms and scrubbed tables stage-set to attract visitors to the Irish country kitchen they're looking for. Lorries delivering crates and pallets of food and drink have blocked the road. Soya milk, herbs and spices, assortments of cheeses, fresh fruit and vegetables have appeared on supermarket shelves. Locals are shopping as if it was the day before Christmas!

As soon as I see the traffic jam, I turn the car and park on the road next to the council houses. I drive past this quiet estate most days but today the place is unrecognisable. The patch of green in front of the fifteen or so flat-fronted semis has been covered in tents in various colours and forms. Houses lucky enough to have a bit of grass have become mini campsites. A woman with dreadlocks sits on a garden path, her legs stretched in front of her as she breastfeeds her baby.

A young couple kneel on the pavement, prodding sausages on a camping-stove.

I get out of the car, walk into town and push my way into the supermarket, letting out a sigh when I see the long queue at the checkout.

Sean and I have been as busy as those in town. The bathroom now has a flushable loo. The spare bedroom's newly plastered walls have been painted pale cream, the rotten floor replaced with new boards that have been sanded and varnished. There's still plenty of work to be done but at least Kate and Sam will have a comfortable room to sleep in.

The phone has finally been connected. I've explained to Kate that the house is still in the process of renovation; that the quiet little town described in my letters has had a make-over.

I spot Kate among the throng coming through Arrivals. I lift my hand and she waves. Seconds later she's in my arms. My eyes are so full of tears I can barely see the man standing next to her. She hugs Sean, turns to the man at her side and, with a look of pride, says, 'This is Sam.'

Sam has a warm smile, a firm grip as he takes my hand and kisses my cheek, a friendly manner when he says to Sean, 'I've heard so much about you; it's good to meet you both at last.'

Sean picks up one of the cases and looks up at the clock, saying, 'We'd better be going. We don't want to hit rush hour. Ennis can be busy.'

After we leave Shannon, I point to places of interest – Bunratty Castle, some of the picturesque places and buildings as we drive through the county town of Ennis, the first glimpse of the sea. We enter Miltown and slow down to a tortoise pace. 'Gosh, what a lot of people,' says Kate. 'Have you been down much?'

'I've become a bit of a home-bird,' says Sean. 'If you want, we'll give it a try this evening.'

We turn onto the Lasheen Road. Sean puts his foot down on the pedal. 'We're nearly there,' I say, looking out of the window at the speeding landscape, remembering the first time I had seen the fuchsia covered hedgerows.

When we arrive at the house, Kate opens the car door, saying, 'Is that Blackie?' She puts out her hand. Blackie sniffs her fingers and Kate strokes him.

Sam stands looking around him saying, 'This is very nice.'

Kate leaves Blackie, puts her arm through Sam's, saying, 'It's bigger than I imagined, and very tidy.' Tubs and pots of bedding plants have replaced the rusting farm equipment that Tom kindly removed. Gravel covers the concrete, hiding the cracks and filling in pot holes.

'Where's Lily?' asks Kate, looking around.

'She stays well away from Blackie,' says Sean. 'She's probably next to the range, savouring the smell of chicken.'

Sean and Sam go to the car boot. I slip my arm through Kate's and we go into the house. 'I hope you like your room,' I say, showing her their bedroom.

Sean appears and puts a case onto the bed. 'Mum's been nagging me for weeks to get it finished; I'm glad you're here so I can have a rest.'

We give them a tour of the house and garden. Sean points to details of work he has done and explains future projects he has in mind. I show them the vegetable patch; the New Zealand Flax I've planted to protect plants from salt-borne wind.

During dinner I decline the offer of a glass of wine from the bottle Sam purchased at the airport. 'I'm driving,' I tell him. 'I'd rather have a drink when we're out.'

It is gone 9.00 p.m. when we leave the house. There are no parking places anywhere near town, so I park outside the cemetery.

We walk the unlit road, stopping for a moment when we enter Miltown, adjusting our senses to the bright lights, the jumble of music from buskers and pubs, the smell of fast-food, the hundreds of people that have taken over the road.

Trestle tables laden with jewellery and candles, bags and haversacks, ethnic clothing displayed on coat-hangers, and a fortune teller sitting by the open door of a caravan adds to the chaos.

I catch the eye of a man with long grey hair. He's wearing a ragged coat and trousers tucked into muddy boots. He gives me a toothless grin, comes towards me, grabs my arm and takes hold of my hand. Two men sat on the pavement with guitars and a man with a fiddle play faster and faster. I try to pull away as I'm spun around, pushed from here to there. Breathless, I scream, 'Stop.' Suddenly, he lets me go. I stand regaining my balance as another woman is pulled from the crowd, her screams swallowed by laughter.

'That's the funniest thing I've seen in a long time,' says Kate.

Sean chuckles. 'You'd better watch out, Anna; he might want another wild dance and come looking for you!'

'If I see him coming, I'll be wild enough to make sure he won't come back!' I say with a grin.

We eventually find a pub with enough room to squeeze into. A table is being vacated and we grab it. A group of musicians put their instruments down and the young girl with them begins to sing. Her long fair hair and ethereal looks match her voice, which is as pure and sweet as a skylark. A hush descends across the pub; even the barman stops serving. Someone dares to speak and an angry 'shush' goes around the room. The end of the song has the effect of a starting pistol and Sean and Sam join the queue at the bar.

Ten minutes later, they arrive with a tray full of drinks, saving them the trouble of having to go back.

It doesn't take long for them to empty the glasses. When Sam puts a new tray of drinks on the table, I say, 'I hope you don't mind, but I think I'll go soon.'

'Mum, you can't. It's early; the night's young.'

'Late nights really don't suit me. I'll be better company tomorrow if I go now.'

'You're such a bore, Anna. You've been complaining about missing the girls. Now Kate's here, you can't wait to go home. Can't you enjoy yourself for once?'

Sam interrupts. 'If Anna wants to leave, let her. We'll get a taxi.'

'Thanks, Sam,' I say, passing my untouched drink to Kate. I pick up my bag and jacket. 'Enjoy yourselves; I'll see you in the morning.'

An angry voice wakes me. Sean's side of the bed is empty. I turn on the light; it's 3.38 a.m. I hear Sam's voice say, 'I'm going. I'll call a taxi,' and I get out of bed, grab my dressing gown and run downstairs. Sam is coming out of the bedroom.

'What on earth's the matter?' I ask.

'I'm leaving. I'm not welcome. Have you got the number of a taxi?'

'What do you mean, you're not welcome? You won't get a taxi. They'll be busy ferrying people home.'

I go into the bedroom. Kate is on the bed, crying into the pillow. I sit beside her, put my hand gently on her shoulder, asking, 'What's happened? Where's Sean?'

She turns to look at me. 'On the sofa. He's been absolutely horrible to Sam!'

Sam comes back into the room. 'He called me useless. He said nursing's women's work and Kate should find a real man. He said I was a wimp!'

I notice that Sam is unsteady, his words slurred. 'That's ridiculous. I'm going to speak to him.'

Kate sits up. 'It won't do any good. He's out of it. When we got back Sam mentioned the bottle of whiskey he bought at the airport. As you can guess, Dad drank most of it! I should have warned him, but it was too late. Once Dad knew there's whiskey... when Dad's like this... I remember why I left home.' She stands up from the bed, goes to Sam, saying, 'Please don't go.'

I look at Sam. 'Kate's right; none of us want you to go. Sean will be full of remorse tomorrow.'

Sam puts his arm around Kate. 'I'm sorry. I shouldn't have lost my temper. I've had too much to drink. Sean and I said things we shouldn't have.'

'We'll all feel better in the morning,' I say. 'Try and get some sleep.'

It's a beautiful morning but it may as well be raining. As soon as I woke, I went downstairs. Sean was asleep on the sofa. I wanted to shake him awake, but knew it would do no good and walked away. There was no sound coming from Kate and Sam's room. I made a cup of coffee and took it outside. I've been sitting with Blackie for an hour or so, just staring into the distance.

I hear the toilet flush. Wondering who it will be, I look through the window. Kate's in the kitchen and I go inside.

'Are you alright, Mum?'

I take the frying pan and put it onto the stove. 'Yes, I'm sorry about last night.'

'It's Dad who should be sorry.'

'How's Sam?'

'He's okay. I told him Dad will regret his behaviour and will be going around with his tail between his legs for the next few days. Do you mind if I make Sam a cup of tea?'

'Of course not.'

'Shall I make Dad one?'

'No. Let him sleep.'

Yesterday's joy seems to have abandoned us. Other than reassuring Sam that it won't happen again, very little is said over our cheerless breakfast. We look up when the sitting-room door opens. 'Is there any tea?' asks Sean.

'The kettle's just boiled.' My voice is cold and unfriendly.

'Is there any breakfast?'

'It's in the oven. Do you remember what you said to Sam?'

'Leave it, Mum. Let's forget it.' Kate turns to Sean and in a quiet voice says, 'Come and sit down. I'll get your breakfast.' She takes it out of the oven and puts it in front of him. 'Mum said she'll take us for a drive, show us a few sights. Are you coming?'

'I think I'll give it a miss. I feel like taking it easy.'

I take them to what we call the locals' beach. It's not the deserted beach I love. Smoke drifts across the sand from the encampment of tents. Bottles, cans and rubbish pile against a wall. People are paddling, skirts held high. Others are in the sea, braving the waves.

We walk the length of the beach; I listen to their chatter. My anger weighs a ton but, somehow, I manage to keep it hidden.

As soon as we enter the house, I know Sean's been drinking – not much, but enough to top up the alcohol from last night's session. Kate will know he went into town – Sean's car is parked at a different angle from when we left. There is no sign of any empties; he will have hidden them. Neither Kate nor I ask what he's been doing. We don't need to.

For the rest of their stay, Sean does his best to make up for his bad behaviour. We share a bottle of wine or two with a meal in the evening, but that's it. We don't go to the pub. The weather stays fine and we're out and about every day. I introduce them to Bridie, Mary, Tom and the children.

Time flies. The dreaded day is upon us. The journey to the airport, the last kiss, the last wave, the last glimpse of Kate's long black hair disappears into the departure lounge.

CHAPTER 7

Our lives have become routine. Sean continues to make improvements on the house, while I carry on advancing through the garden. Other than Bridie and Mary, I see few people. Sean's happy to see no one. The reason I keep sending letters is the prospect of a reply and a visit from Joe the postie!

The only time we go out together is late Sunday morning, when we go to the hotel next to the beach. Now that the holiday season is here the hotel bar is crowded; the only available space is a small table in the foyer, where Sean sits with a beer, I with a glass of wine, watching the hotel guests come and go through the revolving door.

I take my eyes from the door and look at Sean. 'I don't know why we come here. I'd rather go into town and get to know the locals. Why do you like this place?'

'I want to be anonymous. People don't notice us here; they go through that door and have forgotten us by the time they're out the other side.'

What can I say? There's no point in arguing. The only alternative is not going out at all. Not for the first time, I wish I could get inside his head, have a good rummage around and find out what his problem is. 'I'll tell you what l want,' I say, 'I'd like to finish this drink, go home and walk to the lake. It's not far. Bridie and I go there quite often. We occasionally see men fishing. Do you remember the afternoons we used spend by the Avon, you fishing, me reading or sketching? I enjoyed those times. Perhaps you should take your rod up there.'

He doesn't answer. I try again. 'Sean, I would like to go to the lake. With you! It's too nice a day to waste sitting here.'

He picks up his glass, swallows what's left in one go and stubs his cigarette into the ashtray. 'If that's what you want,' he says, picking up his jacket. 'Let's go.' Without waiting for a reply, he strides to the revolving door.

He says nothing on the drive home. He's still in a foul mood when we take the path to the lake. I convince myself that once he sees the lake he will love it.

Skirting puddles, Sean follows behind me. I look back at him; his hands are thrust into his pockets, his face hidden between hunched shoulders and a turned-up collar. 'How much further?' he yells. 'I thought you said it wasn't far.'

'It's not; we're nearly there.' I hurry around the next bend.

'Here it is.' I look down to the lake, pleased to present the view in front of me.

The marshy land falls away to a landslide of rocks and boulders. They give the black water a jagged sculpted frame of slate-grey stone and yellow lichen. On the other side of the lake is a pine forest. The forest is dark and secretive; gives a mystical backdrop to the lake, the reeds that poke their heads through the still water, the moor behind me. The land seems to be listening. I look up into the clear blue sky to see the fluttering specks of skylarks singing their hearts out.

Sean's voice brings me down to earth. 'I doubt if there's any fish. It looks lifeless to me. If there's anything, there'd be a few blokes fishing. Come on; let's go back to the hotel.'

'I don't want to. I want to stay here. Let's go over to the trees; I'd like to explore them.'

'I don't want to look at trees. Come on, Anna, let's go.'

'Please, Sean; I don't want to go to the hotel. Stay with me here.'

'I'm going to the hotel. Are you coming?'

'No. I want to spend the afternoon with you, but not in a bar. I want us to have a walk, then go home and...' I touch his arm.

'You're such a bore, Anna!' He turns away from me, walking back along the path, his solitary figure widening the gap between us.

I wanted so much to spend this afternoon with him, here in this beautiful place. No distractions, no bar, no music except the song of birds. I wanted to touch him, to feel his body next to mine. There had been a few attempts at love-making. When Sean has fallen into bed and tried to kiss me with alcohol fuelled breath, fondled me half-heartedly until he'd fallen asleep, but even that has died a death. I can't remember the last time we touched each other. If I could have kept him away from the bar, held his hand, taken him to the woods, we might have made love, rekindled the love we once shared. The lonely landscape, the emptiness inside me, bring tears that obscure the lake, the forest, the afternoon I was hoping for.

By the time I get home, my sense of loss is as empty as the space where Sean's car had been. My heart tells me my relationship with Sean is falling apart. When I go into the house, I pull the small brown suitcase from under the bed, taking out the photographs and putting them in a folder. Collecting anything I might need, I put them into the empty suitcase. I think for a moment whereabouts to hide it, then I go to the guest room and put it into the back of the wardrobe.

I've been counting the days, longing for this moment to arrive. It only took minutes for Alice and Adam to put their things into their rooms, for Sean and Adam to follow Ella into the garden. I'm about to suggest to Alice that we join them when she says, 'Mum, I've something to tell you.'

I don't know why her announcement comes as such a surprise; after all, they always said they would have another child.

'I would have told you before,' she says, 'but I didn't want to tell you over the phone. The baby's due in January. Ella's so excited. I'm surprised she didn't burst it out as soon as she saw you. I think seeing Blackie made her forget about babies!'

I look out at the rectangle of rough grass that was part of the field – now promoted to a lawn. Sean and Adam are securing an old tyre and a length of rope to a tree while Ella patiently watches. I think about the coming baby, another grandchild too far away.

'Mum?'

I turn to look at her. 'Sorry. I was thinking about my new grandchild. Congratulations. What exciting news! When in January?'

'The sixth. Adam's telling Dad now. I wanted to tell you by myself.'

She comes towards me. The grips have fallen from her hair. Alice's hair has always been a source of irritation. Alice, who manages to keep everything and everyone in order, cannot control her unruly curls. We put our arms around each other. 'I've missed you, Mum.'

'Me too; I've missed you terribly.'

'Are you all right?'

'I'm fine.' I take my arms away from her and look out of the window. Ella is charging towards us across the grass. 'Here comes Ella,' I say, glad of an excuse to change the subject.

The door bursts open. 'Mummy! Nana! I've got a swing!'

I pick her up, her boots leaving muddy trails across my skirt. 'How exciting, and you're going to be a big sister!'

She wriggles out of my arms. 'Yes, I am, but come and see my swing! Mummy, come and see my swing!'

Blackie is panting by the door, ready for another chase with Ella. Alice and I loop arms as we follow them to the trees. Sean lifts Ella onto the tyre, making her shriek with laughter as he pushes her.

'Congratulations, Adam,' I say, giving him a big hug.

'Thanks, yeah; it's great. We're delighted.'

Sean lifts Ella from the swing and holds her as she tries to climb the rope to the branch above. 'You should think about moving over here,' he shouts over his shoulder. 'It's a great place for kids. All this space! It's what they need.'

'I don't know,' shrugs Adam. 'It's a big step. Besides, my business is going well; I've regular customers.'

'You'll get work here. They're crying out for plumbers.'

'There's also my mum and dad to consider. They idolise Ella.'

I am left thinking, *'So do I.'*

Sean's been a lot happier since they've been here. Last night, he and Adam went into town. I don't know what time they got back; I didn't hear them come in, but there were no arguments and Sean made it into bed. This morning, they were up early, sitting at the kitchen table drawing plans for the new porch. Unlike Sam, Adam knows his father-in-law well and gives him as good as he gets. Having Alice here has made me realise how important family is. Listening to Ella's chatter, watching her enthusiasm for each new day has brought life into the house.

The days are slipping by. I can't bear the thought of them leaving. I creep into Ella's room; she is fast asleep, exhausted by a day of sand and sea.

Sean and Adam are watching a hurling match on the television. Alice is sat outside drinking tea. I go out to her and ask, 'Do you want to go for a walk? I'd like to show you the lake. If we leave now we'll be in time to see the sun set.'

'Sounds lovely,' says Alice, standing up. 'I'll tell Adam. Ella's out for the count. He won't hear a peep out of her.'

We've been standing at the water's edge, listening to the skylark's song for a while. The beauty of the place is overwhelming. Suddenly, I notice how low the sun is. 'I didn't realise how late it is,' I say. We leave the lake as the sky turns to a pallet of rose and forget-me-not blue. By the time we reach the road, the sky is crimson. We stand side by side, watching the sky's ever-changing colours. Alice puts her arm through mine, saying, 'I can understand what the attraction is... but are you happy? You've lost your sparkle. Even with Ella you're different. You don't laugh anymore.'

What can I say – that I made a huge mistake? Sean loves it here. He won't want to go back to England. He doesn't need people the way I do. He doesn't need anything other than his fiddle, money for booze and me. He won't admit it, but Sean needs me. I think of the suitcase hidden in the wardrobe. I don't know what would happen to him if I were to leave.

'Mum...?'

'I think we'd better be going,' I say, hoping to stop her questioning me.

We walk back towards the house. 'What's the matter?' she asks.

'I miss you. I miss work and my friends. I miss being able to talk about... well, you know what your dad's like. Bridie won't understand. I can't tell her, not about things like that. Mary's busy, what with the farm and the children. The Irish keep their problems to themselves. When we were in Bristol I had people to talk to, family, friends. Work took up a large part of my life. Now Sean and I are here, we're together most of the time and... well, it's been difficult.'

'I noticed you've started a painting. Your palette is so dark. Your paintings used to be full of colour.'

'I took photos of storm clouds. I was out for a walk with Bridie. I was planning a seascape. I haven't got round to finishing it. The garden takes up most of my time. It's when I'm at my happiest.'

By the time we reach the lane, it's getting dark. The light from the kitchen window gives a glimpse of a cosy room, peacefully idyllic.

We stop at the door. 'Is there any chance of one of your friends coming to stay?' says Alice. 'What about Liz or Vicky? Has Sue got any leave due?'

'I don't think so. They want to spend their leave with family or somewhere hot.'

'Why don't you come back with us? Meet up with your mates. Kate would love to see you.'

The thought is attractive. 'I don't know. Your dad won't want to be on his own.'

'He can come as well.'

'Are you sure? Kate told me that she and Sam have found a flat to rent. I'd love to see it and it'll be good see how the tenants are getting on.'

'I don't know,' Sean frowns. 'What about Lily?'

'What about Lily? I'm sure Bridie or Mary will feed her.'

'We can't impose on people; anyway, I want to make a start on the porch before winter sets in. You go if you want to.'

'I'd like to. I want to see Kate's new flat. And there's the tenants, I think it's wise to let them know we're around sometimes.'

'How long will you go for?'

'I don't know. A week or two. I'd like to meet up with a few friends while I'm there.'

Alice was determined I was going to leave with them. She persuaded Sean that checking on the tenants was a good idea and that a few nights out with the girls would 'buck me up'.

She couldn't coax Sean into coming. I hate to admit it, but I was pleased when he refused.

Swansea harbour is a welcome sight. Just driving off the boat onto British shores lifts my spirits. The familiarity of policemen, British number plates, red post boxes and traffic wardens go straight to my heart. We cross the Severn Bridge and in next to no time Adam is parking the car outside their house. Minutes later, Kate is ringing the door bell and we are sat at the table drinking tea. 'What plans have you got?' asks Kate.

'I'd like to see your flat. I told Sean I'll call in on the tenants. Tomorrow I'm meeting the girls in town.'

The last time I was out with the girls was in another life. The places are the same, so are Liz, Sue and Vicky, but I'm not. I'm the visitor – the outsider. I feel like a tourist as we wander the city. Everywhere is busy – chains of traffic, people of all nationalities, rushing, dawdling, gazing, queuing for buses, taxis, coffee. After the wide open spaces of Ireland, the city seems small and cramped, alive and buzzing.

We enter a waterside café, find a table by a window and make ourselves comfortable on chrome chairs. A bright yellow ferry has just docked. A sunburnt man in faded jeans and T-shirt helps passengers alight.

'What are we having, girls?' asks Sue when a good-looking waiter appears at our table.

'Wine, of course,' replies Liz, with a red lipstick smile.

It's not long before there's a bottle of wine on the table and the waiter's taking our order for olives and Italian salads.

Sue pours the wine. We each pick up a glass.

'To Anna,' says Vicky. 'Good to see you back. Tell us what you've been up to. We want to know everything.'

'Well, at the moment I'm in culture shock; like I've arrived from the moon. There's nothing like this where I live, just fields, more fields and the Atlantic Ocean. The neighbours are friendly. Mary, who we bought the house from, occasionally calls in, and Bridie, another neighbour, and I go walking. That's if the weather's okay. We get a lot of rain. I'm lonely sometimes. My neighbours are lovely but they're not like you; they're respectable.'

Liz snorts with laughter. 'What a bloody cheek!'

'They are. I don't know what I'd do without them; I think I'd go mad. Where I live, women's lives revolve around home, family and church. Mary doesn't do girls' nights. Bridie must be in her seventies; she never married. I'd put a bet on it that she's still a virgin.'

'Christ!' exclaims Liz. 'How old did you say she was? I didn't know virgins existed over the age of sixteen!'

'I'm sure there are a few around, even in England. Bridie wouldn't know or understand about men and their selfish ways, and Mary hasn't got time to listen to my woes, and she wouldn't want to tell me hers. Though I doubt if she has any; Tom's lovely – he's not a drinker.'

'So, Sean's still pissing it up,' says Liz.

'Yes, he is and I'm finding it difficult to manage without the mutual support group, meaning you lot.'

'You can always ring,' says Sue.

'It's difficult. Sean's always there. He seldom goes out and I can hardly complain about him when he's with me.'

'God, I wish you weren't so far away,' says Sue. 'You must come over more often.'

'It was hard enough convincing Sean that I needed to come this time. Alice had to work on him.'

The waiter arrives with the food. I stop talking as he lays it in front of us. As he moves away, I pick up my knife and fork, saying, 'Anyway, don't let's spoil the day. I want to forget about Sean and Ireland.'

'Have you heard anything from David?' asks Vicky before popping an olive into her mouth.

'Yes, I gave him a ring before I left. I thought it would be nice to meet up. He said he's busy, though he's giving me a lift to the airport.'

I stand by the window waiting for David's silver Audi to arrive. I've been dreading this moment. Nothing will lift the sadness of having to leave. I see David's car turn into Alice's road and I go into the hallway and open the door. I watch him park, waiting while he walks up the path. He kisses my cheek and I realise how much I've wanted to spend some time with him. He looks me up and down. 'You've lost weight. I'd have thought the rich Irish butter and cream would have put pounds on.'

'Kerry has the cream; Clare's has the rock and peat bog. Digging the field's taken the weight off.'

'Are you ready?'

'Just about.' I'd already said a tearful goodbye to Kate. I still carry the ache in my heart after leaving Ella in the nursery.

Alice comes into the hallway. 'Have you got everything?'

'I think so.'

I put my arms around her. 'Thanks, I needed this break. I'll ring when I get home.'

We drive away and I turn to look back at Alice one last time. David questions me on what Sean is doing on the house – I didn't want to talk about Sean and Ireland, and all too soon we are in the airport. 'While you check in, I'll get us a coffee,' says David.

When I join David at the table, I pick up the coffee and thank him. 'What have you been up to?' I ask. 'It's a shame we weren't able to meet up.'

'I've met a woman; her name's Diane. You'll like her. We've been seeing a lot of each other.' His words are as sharp as a surgeon's knife. 'Her neighbour's an old customer of mine. I was passing his house and called in to say hello and she was there; her car was in the garage so I gave her a lift into town. She's a teacher; she...'

I stop listening and ask myself why I'm feeling this way. I've met many of David's girlfriends. I've always been happy for him to have a woman in his life. He is waiting for me to say something. 'Oh, that's nice. I expect I'll meet her some time. Sorry, I don't think I've time to finish the coffee. I don't want to leave everything to the last minute; I'd rather go now.' I pick up my bag. He follows me to the escalator and gives me a peck on the cheek.

'Tell Sean to give me a ring if he wants me to look at those plans. He can always post me a copy,' he says.

The stairs carry me towards the departure lounge. I look down when I reach the top. David waves. I give a brief smile before turning away.

CHAPTER 8

I'm dreaming of a White Christmas... The song's banal sentiments pour out of the supermarket's taped music system. Occasionally I catch myself singing along, and it's then that I hate the jingly, jangly tunes the most. I won't be *"Decking the Halls with Holly"* or *"Rocking around the Christmas Tree"*.

The cottage will remain looking like any other day. No tinsel, no holly, no mistletoe. The cards we've received are stacked in a pile on the coffee table. Mary's gift, a bottle of wine, stands on the dresser; Bridie's present to me – a bottle of Bailey's Cream – is hidden in the wardrobe next to the small brown suitcase, away from Sean's eyes.

I've written and posted the obligatory Christmas cards, tucked cheques into Kate and Alice's, put a letter into my sister's apologising for not having been in touch and that when the house is ready she and James must come and visit. I've given chocolates to Mary and Bridie. Made sure we've enough food to last the Christmas period.

There will be just the two of us this Christmas, and I dread it. Other years, in that other life, we'd spent it with one or both of the girls – being with them had made Christmas tolerable. This year Sean insisted we spend it here in Ireland. I've argued and sulked but finally gave in on the promise that we would go to Bristol for the New Year and stay until Alice's baby is born.

It is Christmas morning. My mood matches the cold, silent house. The view through the window – a grey sky and a barren landscape – reflect my feelings. I walk as quietly as I can across the kitchen floor and, as noiselessly as possible, put my cup into the sink. I've disconnected the phone. I don't want to listen to friendly voices that might make me cry. Nor do I want to disturb Sean; the longer he sleeps the shorter our day together. When he's awake, before he starts drinking and drifts out of reach, I'll ring the girls.

Lily starts to cry; I pick her up and take her outside. Seeing Blackie, she jumps from my arms and runs back into the house. I follow her, watching as she runs up the stairs and noses open the bedroom door. Seconds later Sean calls, 'Is there any tea?'

I pour him his tea, giving it to him and saying, 'I'll ring the girls. Ella will have opened her presents by now.'

'...Wow, you are a lucky girl... Yes, that's right, we'll see you in a couple of days... Granddad and I will be there to look after you when your baby's being born... Can't wait to see you... Let me pass you to Granddad... Bye darling.'

Now the phone calls are made, Sean takes the remains of last night's bottle of whiskey into the sitting-room, and the shutter falls firmly between us. I put on my new raincoat – bought with the money Sean gave me – and I go outside.

Blackie joins me and we walk, past the fairy lights flashing in Mary's bay window, past Bridie's bungalow – its curtains drawn until she returns from her sister in Dublin – past empty fields, blackthorn bushes and leafless hedgerow and onto the path that leads to the lake.

A mist has crept across the moor, has fastened itself to everything it touches, floats like a phantom between the dark water and silent sky, leaves my hair and Blackie's fur wet with droplets. It's when the cold creeps into my bones and I start to shiver that we reluctantly make our way home.

The sound of the Beach Boys singing "Good Vibrations" greets me when I step into the house. Sean is in the sitting-room listening to music. Another bottle has gone from the dresser. This Christmas will be no different from any other except this time there's just the two of us.

I automatically prepare the vegetables, then, leaving them in the oven with the chicken, I go into the little bedroom, take the bottle of Bailey's Cream from the wardrobe, open it and put my feet up on the bed and the bottle to my lips.

The Bailey's has done nothing to deaden the repulsion I feel – Sean's chin is awash with grease and gravy, his cheek is pressed against the pulverised remains of roast potatoes on the table. They were hot from the oven when I pushed up Sean's sleeve, squashed them onto the delicate skin of his wrist, rubbed the steaming vegetable along the length of his arm – I was too angry to feel their heat, Sean too drunk to notice what I was doing.

Sean's eyes are closed. He doesn't move as I clear and wash the dishes, is far away in a place of his own when I go back to the little bedroom.

I've lost all concept of time. I don't know how long I've been laying on the bed watching the grey day darken to night. I hear a chair scrape across the kitchen floor, see the light shine through the gap around my door, hear the clink of bottles, the sitting-room door open and close, the foot on the stair, the creak on the floorboard, the certainty that this will be our last Christmas together.

For what seems like an hour, I've been standing by our luggage, reminding Sean about the time. The cardboard box he covered and lined with three, quite decent, jumpers is finally ready – I also want Lily to be comfortable and Mary's been given enough food to feed her for a month. When Lily gets cold she'll realise the box is the warmest place to be. My departing gift to Blackie is a lamb shank. When that's gone, he'll do what he did before we came – beg at neighbours' doors.

As the boat leaves Cork Harbour, I start to relax. I'm not sure how long we'll be in England – it depends when Alice's baby is born. It's due on the sixth of January, so we will have over two weeks, maybe more.

Kate is having a New Year party. David has been invited. Alice told me he's taking Diane. Like all his girlfriends, she'll be attractive and well dressed. I've nothing suitable to wear to a party; Kate and I are around the same size and I wonder if she'll have something I can borrow.

I press Kate's door bell. A few moments later the door opens and she is in front of me.

'I know I'm early,' I say. 'Sean's in B&Q and I didn't want to go with him. To tell you the truth, I couldn't wait to see you.'

'Don't stand there. Come in,' she says, pulling me into her arms.

'I would have come sooner,' I say, following her up the stairs, 'but Alice is tired and I've been helping her as much as I can. I'm hoping the baby won't arrive tonight. I've told Adam to ring if they need me. A taxi will get me back there in minutes. If the worse comes to the worst, he can drop Ella off here.'

We stop on the landing. 'We've done a lot of decorating and bought a few things from IKEA,' she says as she opens the door.

'Wow, it's gorgeous! What a change.' I point to the white sofa, 'Is it yours?'

'Yes, the landlady said we could add a few things of our own. I'm really pleased with it. It was reduced because of a tiny flaw on the seam but it's hardly noticeable.'

'I think you're brave having a party. The sofa's lovely but what if someone spills a drink on it?'

'Don't worry. I'll keep an eye on things. Come and have a cup of tea. Sam's out doing some last-minute shopping. You can give me a hand with the food.'

We spend the rest of the afternoon cutting up lumps of cheese and making dips and sandwiches. When we finish I ask, 'Do you have anything I can wear? We don't even go to the pub now so there's no point buying anything new.'

'Have a look in my wardrobe. I'm wearing the red dress, but help yourself to anything else.' I leave her tidying the kitchen and go into the bedroom. 'Goodness,' I think when I slide the wardrobe door open and find it crammed with clothes. I pull out a straight leopard print dress in a silky material and a black dress with a flared skirt. The leopard print fits like a glove, though I feel a little bare around the neck and wonder if it's too tight. 'Kate,' I call, 'what do you think of this? Come and see.'

'Oh yes,' she says as she comes into the room. 'I like it.'

I start to undo the buttons. 'I'll try on the black one.'

'You don't want that old thing,' she says, tossing it aside. 'You look great in what you're wearing. I've got the shoes to match.' She kneels on the floor pulling out shoe after shoe from the bottom of the wardrobe. 'Here's one,' she exclaims, 'and here's the other!'

Feeling like an ugly sister, I squeeze my foot into the shoe and tighten the strap, saying, 'I don't know if I can walk in these.'

'You're not going hiking; you can always take them off later. Go and wet your hair; I'm going to use my straighteners on you. You'll be the belle of the ball tonight!'

People are starting to arrive. I'm wondering where Sean has got to, when he walks into the room. His eyes open wide when he sees me. 'My God! What have you done with your hair, and why are you dressed like that?'

On hearing his voice, Kate comes out of the kitchen, gives him a hug before saying, 'Mum looks great. You're jealous someone will take a fancy to her. Give the wine to Sam; he's in the kitchen sorting out the drinks table.'

Each time the bell rings, each time the sitting room door opens, I look to see if it's David. Just when I'm thinking he's not coming, he arrives. He looks around and waves at me from across the room. He takes the hand of the woman beside him and leads her towards me. 'I hardly recognised you,' he says before kissing my cheek. 'Let me introduce you. Diane, this is Anna.'

As I thought, Diane is extremely attractive. Her clothes look expensive; her dark sleek hair is styled to perfection. I offer her my hand, saying, 'It's nice to meet you.'

'Is Sean here?' asks David.

'Yes, he's in the kitchen, hogging the drinks table I suspect.'

'I'd better get in there quick then.'

David grabs Diane's hand. I watch them move through the crowded room, wishing I'd insisted on wearing the black dress, which would have gone very well with my boots.

David and Diane have been in and out of the kitchen a number of times. Sean hadn't left it since he arrived, and I feel apprehensive – I remember feeling this way at other times, other parties, how responsible I'd felt for Sean's behaviour, how often I'd apologised for broken glasses and spilt drinks. I'm about to go to the kitchen and find out what condition he's in when Sean, holding a glass full of red wine, stumbles through the door. I freeze. People part like waves. Kate shouts, 'Careful!' and everyone takes their eyes from Kate's horrified face to the red stain spreading its way across the sofa's white upholstery.

Holding tightly to his empty glass, Sean turns around and staggers back to the kitchen. A young woman rushes past him, saying, 'It's all right; white wine removes stains.' She comes back with a bottle of white wine and pours it onto the sofa. The wine turns to a pale shade of pink as it travels down the arm onto the padded seat. The girl laughs nervously, saying, 'I really thought it would work.' With that, Kate disappears into the kitchen; what she is saying to Sean is loud and clear enough for all to hear.

A group of friends are stood looking and discussing the sofa; when Kate comes back into the room, she and Sam join them. I notice that David and Diane are arguing. She pushes him. He walks away and she watches him with angry eyes.

The shoes are killing me and the straps are beginning to cut into my ankles. I bend over, undo the buckle and take them off. When I stand up I notice Diane is talking to Kate. Leaving the shoes on the floor, I walk barefoot to the kitchen. Sean is slumped in a chair. David is opening a bottle of wine, and I walk towards him. He puts the opener and the bottle onto the table. I put arms around him and my lips to his. A hand is on my shoulder. I turn away from David and look directly at Sean's face. 'See,' my eyes tell him, 'this is what will happen if you don't change your ways.' For a brief moment it seemed my message had registered; when he falls back into the chair I know it's already forgotten. David pats my bottom, picks up the bottle of wine and leaves the kitchen, saying, 'You should wear clothes like that more often. I like the effect they have on you.'

I look at Sean, asking myself, 'Is this all I am left with?'

Stella is born three days later. I hold her against my shoulder; she's now ten days old.

'Can't we stay a few more days?' I ask Sean.

'No. We've been here a few more days. We can't expect Mary to keep feeding Lily. She'll be running out of food and, besides, I've work to do.'

I want to beg him, insist I stay and that he goes back without me but I know he won't agree. When he says, 'We'll catch the afternoon ferry tomorrow,' his mind is made up. He picks up his jacket. 'I'll take the car to the garage, fill up with petrol and check the tyres.' I stand at the window watching him walk down the path. I'm there long after he has driven away. The warmth of the baby, the softness of her hair on my lips, only fuels my anger.

CHAPTER 9

Primroses dot the grassy banks, catkins appear in the hedgerow. Leaves are unfolding on the rowan tree, new shoots pushing up through the soil. I look up into a clear blue sky and watch the house martins' aerobatics. They started arriving a few days ago, flying straight to the outbuildings to take residency in the little mud nests they vacated last year. My eyes land upon the dent in the bumper of my car, suddenly darkening the lovely day, reminding me not to forget that dreadful night two weeks ago.

Sean's binge began on the Saturday afternoon. It lasted late into the night. As usual, he started drinking again the following morning and carried on through the rest of the day. By 9.00 p.m. he was unconscious. It was then that I decided to spend the night in the little bedroom.

I don't know how long I'd been asleep, or what time it was, when I was jolted awake by such a terrific bang that the wall next to where I was sleeping shook. I jumped out of bed, ran through the kitchen, opened the front door and saw Sean fumbling with his key. Pushing past him, I saw my car smashed against the wall next to where I'd been sleeping.

Furious, I rushed back into the house and found Sean vomiting into the kitchen sink. 'What on earth did you think you were doing?' I shouted. 'I'd have thought you'd learned your lesson! Do you want to be banned again? Actually, I hope you are. I hope the Garda catch you and lock you up!'

He turned to face me, propped himself against the sink, saying, 'Shut up, you silly bitch.'

I put my face to his, could see the broken veins on his cheek, the blood-shot in his eyes, smell the whiskey and vomit on his breath when I hissed, 'You don't believe me, but

I'm telling you I'll walk away from here and never come back.'

'Fuck off then,' he said. I walked away, heard his laugh as I closed the bedroom door.

I couldn't sleep, was still awake when daylight filtered through the curtain. I heard Sean's footsteps coming down the stairs and pulled the covers tightly around me. I wanted to withdraw from Sean, the house, Ireland, even the garden, to disconnect myself from life itself.

It was late morning when I made myself get dressed. I walked into the kitchen – the vomit in the sink had been replaced with the smell of disinfectant. Sean was sat at the table smoking. When he saw me, he stood up, saying, 'I've just made a pot of tea. Let me pour you one.' He went to the range, poured the tea with his back towards me and said, 'I'm sorry about the car. It was an accident. There's something wrong with the hand brake.' He brought the tea to me then went outside.

I heard him reverse the car; glancing out of the window, I saw him looking beneath the car's bonnet. Half an hour later he came inside, telling me, 'I've tightened the hand brake; it's fine now. Would you like a drive to Ennis? We can have a bit of lunch out, look around the shops.' He spoke as though we'd had nothing more than a minor tiff.

I went to Ennis with him, all the hurtful things he's said, the nights I've lain awake alive in my memory.

A few days later David rang; he wanted to know if he and Diane could come and stay.

The ring from the phone scatters my thoughts and I go into the house.

I haven't spoken to David since the party; the sound of his voice causes a rush of embarrassment and I quickly say, 'Sean's out; he's gone to pick up some roof slates. I'll get him to call you back.'

'He doesn't need to do that. I wanted to let you know that Diane and I aren't together anymore.'

'Does that mean she won't be coming?' I say, hiding my pleasure with a serious voice.

'She's still coming; we're friends – at least I think we are. She said she's been looking forward to going away and I should do the decent thing and let her have her holiday.'

'Why did you finish with her?'

'She expected me to spend all my free time with her. It was getting to the point when she was telling me what to wear and how I should live my life. We've had some blazing rows.'

'So you'll want separate rooms?'

I hear Sean's car turn at the top of the lane. 'Sean's arrived,' I say. 'Let him know the details.' I go outside. 'David's on the phone,' I tell him. Sean goes into the house.

I walk to the old stone wall, sit looking across the garden, stroking Blackie's head, thinking about David and the party. When I kissed David in front of Sean, it wasn't only to ignite a spark of jealousy. I kissed him because I wanted to.

I look in the mirror; the half hour I spent reading outdated magazines while waiting for Maureen to finish Mrs O'Connell's perm was well worth the time. The hair cut isn't bad. Clean jeans and T-shirt, the merest touch of lipstick and anyone would believe I look like this all the time.

A car turns at the top of the lane. I look out of the window and see David's car. I run down the stairs, wait outside for the car door to open; as soon as David's feet touch the ground I wipe away my resolve to be objective and fling my arms around him. I hear Sean's voice, look behind me and see Sean striding across the yard. David leaves me and they grab each other by the hand, slap each other on the back and disappear into the house. I look away and see Diane struggling with a case. She looks completely out of place in her high heels, tight-fitting dress and cream jacket. I go over to her. She puts the case down, runs her fingers through her hair, brushes it away from her face saying, 'He's no thought or consideration for me. I've had a dreadful journey.'

'I bet you could do with a drink,' I say, taking the case from her.

'I'd love a cup of tea. You'd have thought David would've carried in the cases before running off.'

'I expect him and Sean have loads to talk about.'

She goes back to the car and takes a cake tin from the back seat. 'I made this lemon drizzle cake. It's David's favourite.'

'That sounds good. Sean complains there's never any cake in the house'.

'Where are they?' she says when we go into the house.

I look out of the window. 'They're in the garden. Let me show you your room, it's a single bed but very comfortable.'

She doesn't move. 'What's the matter?' I ask.

'I'm sleeping with David.'

'I thought... He said you were just friends.'

'We are. That doesn't stop us sleeping together.'

'I'm sorry. Sean said that David... it doesn't matter; there's a double bed in David's room.' I take her to the room prepared for David. 'You sort yourself out,' I say. 'I'll put the kettle on. Thanks for the cake; I'll put it on the table.'

The men are loading logs into the wheelbarrow. I walk over to them. 'Tea will be ready in about five minutes.' I look at David. 'She told me you're sharing a room.'

'Yes, anything to keep her quiet.'

'Well, it seems a bloody stupid idea to me,' says Sean, heaving another log into the wheelbarrow.

'I agree,' I say. 'You might build her hopes up.'

'It's just during this holiday,' says David, looking uncomfortable. 'When it's over, that'll be it; I shan't see her again.'

'Well I think you're daft,' I say. 'Anyway, don't be long. The kettle will be boiling by now.'

Diane and I are sat at the table; she is well into her second piece of cake. 'What are they doing?' she asks. 'The tea's cold.'

'It'll keep warm on the range. If it's stewed, it's their hard luck. They've probably forgotten all about us.'

She finishes eating and takes another slice of cake. 'He's so unkind. Before we'd left he had me in tears, and I'd done nothing wrong. On the ferry he scarcely spoke. When I tried to speak to him he almost jumped down my throat, for no reason.'

'Well, you're here now,' I say soothingly. 'He's probably tired. I know he's supposed to be retired, but he's still doing jobs for old customers. Give him a few days and he'll start to relax. Ah, here they are.'

I'm woken by the sound of sobbing. Sean is sleeping soundly beside me. When I went to bed last night they were finishing what was left of the wine. Even Diane was in a good mood.

The sobbing grows louder. Sean doesn't stir as I get out of bed and go downstairs. Diane is sat at the kitchen table. 'What's the matter?' I ask.

'Him! He was late coming to bed and when he did he turned his back to me. I only wanted a cuddle but he completely ignored me.'

'Look, Diane, go into the other bedroom; it's ready for you. You'll feel better away from him.' I get her a tissue. 'Come on, you're tired after the journey. Go and get some sleep. You'll feel better in the morning.'

She takes the tissue, stands up, wipes her eyes as I propel her towards the little bedroom. 'Goodnight,' I say. 'I'll see you in the morning.'

I'm just dropping off to sleep when again I hear her crying. With a sigh of exasperation, I get out of bed and go downstairs. Diane has gone back to the kitchen. Trying to keep the irritation out of my voice I ask her, 'What's the matter?'

'It's no good. I can't sleep knowing he's the other side of the wall.'

I go into the bedroom, gather together the pillow and duvet, give them to her, saying, 'You can sleep on the sofa. It's quite comfortable. I'll see you in the morning.'

Diane's black mood casts a cloud across the breakfast table. Even David's cheery disposition has left him. His voice breaks the silence when he asks, 'What have you been up to, Anna? Have you done any painting since you've been here?'

'I started one but haven't got round to finishing it. Gardening's become my love; I can't keep away from it.'

'Rain or shine, Anna's out there,' says Sean. 'I hardly see her. I've been thinking, it'll do us good to get away from Miltown for a few days. Aly Bain's playing in Listowel tomorrow. He's a great fiddle player; it's bound to be a good session. We've got a couple of tents. We'll take the ferry across the Shannon; from there it's a forty-minute drive.'

'I don't know,' says Diane looking slightly interested.

'Why not?' I say. 'You and I can share a tent. We can leave the men to enjoy their smelly socks and snoring without us. We'll look around the town. Do girlie things. I'll ring the tourist board and make sure there's a camp site; if there is, let's go'.

The Shannon is as calm as a pond. We look for dolphins; watch Clare's landscape shrink as Kerry's mountains grow.

When we leave the ferry we follow the signs to Listowel. It's three-thirty when we arrive. By the time we find the camp site, debate where to put two small tents, it's gone 5 o'clock. We walk into town and find the shops closed. 'Perhaps they'll be open tomorrow,' I say.

'I doubt it,' says Diane. 'Not on a Sunday. Anyway, I'm hungry. There must be a restaurant around.'

'I'm going to the pub,' says Sean. 'I want to find out where Aly's playing. Do you fancy a drink David?'

We watch the men walk away. Diane scowls. 'You'd have thought they would have joined us. What if we can't find them?'

'Sean's never one for restaurants. The town's small; we're bound to find them. There can't be many pubs and we only have to mention Aly Bain.'

We search the streets looking for a place to eat; eventually we find a café open and go inside. A young woman is wiping the tables with a strong-smelling chemical spray and a grey dishcloth; she looks up when she sees us, saying, 'We're closed.'

'Is there anywhere we can get a meal?' I ask.

'You can try O'Malley's down the end of the street.'

We've been in O'Malley's a good few hours; it's comfortable, not too crowded, with good food and an open fire. The warmth and the steak and Guinness pie has made me sleepy. I think about Sean. I've no need to guess what condition he'll be in.

Diane scrapes the last spoonful of apple pie from her dish and says, 'I wonder what the men are up to. They must be wondering where we are. We'd better start trying to find them.'

'They've probably forgotten all about us,' I say.

'Well, I think we should go looking for them.'

~ 78 ~

'I'd like a coffee.' I order the coffee, taking my time with occasional sips. It's Diane's constant fidgeting and looking at her watch that wins.

The pub where Aly is playing is tiny. I stand on tiptoe and look across the crowded room. Sean is sat amongst a group of musicians. He's how I expected him to be – his fiddle out of sight, a twisted roll-up between his lips. I spot David, turn to Diane and indicate where he is. We squeeze our way towards him. I tap his shoulder. Shouting above the noise, I ask, 'Is Aly here?'

David shakes his head. 'Not yet. He may not arrive till gone ten. By all accounts there's a problem with transport.'

'What!' exclaims Diane. 'That's an hour away. I can't stay here. The smoke's stinging my eyes. O'Malley's is nearby; it's much better than this place.'

'Well, go there,' David tells her.

'I want you to come.'

'I'm staying here.'

'That's the trouble with you; you're selfish. You brought me here. The least you can do is be with me.'

'Diane! I told you, I'm staying here. If you want to go to O'Malley's, GO!'

Tears spring in her eyes. She turns away and pushes her way through the crowd.

I look at Sean precariously sat on a chair, dangerously near to falling off. A man shoves past me and I'm pushed against David. The words leave my lips without a thought. 'If only it was you and I, just the two of us, David.'

He puts his lips to my ear. 'Maybe we should get together sometime.'

Suddenly, I want to run and I turn away, saying, 'I must find Diane.' Without stopping, I push my way out into the night; run through the streets, adrenaline fuelling my feet, my thoughts racing ahead of me; his words... sometime... sometime... repeated with each stride I take.

For the rest of their stay I avoid being too close to him. That is until now; the morning they're due to leave. I see him amongst the pines, looking towards the Kerry Mountains. He hears my step, turns and smiles. 'I'm going to miss you,' I say.

'You know where to find me, Anna.'

CHAPTER 10

'You know how I feel about christenings,' says Sean, 'and what about the garden? A week without rain and all your hard work has been in vain.'

'Sean, this is Ireland. A week without rain is an improbability. I'd have thought you'd want to be at your granddaughter's christening.'

'I told you. I don't like christenings, or anything to do with religion. When I die, don't you dare let any priest perform his mumbo jumbo over my body; anyway, why on earth do they want a christening? Neither of them go to church. I thought they were atheists'.

'They are. They're having Stella christened for the same reasons Ella was. Adam's mum and dad are staunch churchgoers. It's important to them.'

'Well, I think they should stick to their convictions. Let the children decide for themselves when they're old enough.'

'I agree, but the fact is there's going to be a christening and I'm going to be there. You can do what you like.'

'I'm not going!' He takes a deep breath and in a quiet voice says, 'I'm sorry, Anna, but I really can't stand churches.'

With a little persuasion, I think I could get him to come, especially if I agree to go for just a few days, but I need to be there at least a week; as well as family and the tenants, there are friends I want to see.

I change tack. 'Look, Sean, I'll talk to Alice. I'm sure she'll understand. And you're right, the tomato plants will need watering, and I'd like you to keep an eye on the cabbages; those pesky caterpillars will turn them to lace the minute my back's turned.'

He stands up from the table with a sigh of relief, goes to the dresser, saying, 'You know how I hate all that standing around sipping sherry. And Adam's mum really gets on my tits.' He picks up his keys. 'I'm going to O'Dwyer's. Do you need anything in town?'

As the door closes behind him I have a flash of guilt. To justify myself, I think of the reasons Sean should stay at home. He really does not like socialising. His hatred of churches is genuine. More importantly, he's very likely to get drunk. Without him being there I'll be able to relax.

Tomorrow I fly to England. Intent on leaving the garden in a manageable state, I search between the cabbage leaves for caterpillars and drop them into a jam jar. My thoughts go from Sean to David and I ask myself if I could ever leave Sean – the answer is clearly NO! Other than a wave from Tom when he drives past on his tractor, Sean will see no one. He could be dead in his bed and not be missed. As for David, my head says I should stay away from him.

I hear the phone ring and I look towards the house. I look up again when Sean calls my name and shouts, 'David wants a word with you.' With mixed feelings, I screw the lid onto the jam jar, put it onto the ground and walk to the house.

Sean hands me the telephone.

I say little as David tells me he'd called in on Alice. She told him about the christening and that I'm going to be staying with her. He offers to pick me up from the airport and I quickly tell him, 'Kate's offered to collect me.' Desperate to get away from Sean's enquiring eyes and David's voice, I say, 'I must get back to the garden. I'll pass you to Sean.'

David's last words to me are, 'I'll see you at Alice's.'

It's amazing how quickly, how easily, how without a thought for Sean, the cottage, Blackie – even the garden! – I settle into Alice's home. I am sat in the lounge enjoying the peace and quiet. Ella is in bed. Adam is visiting his sister and her new baby. The television stands silent. The only sound is the gentle snuffle of the baby as she feeds. Alice takes Stella from her breast, leans her forward and gently rubs her back. She looks towards me and says, 'There's something I want to tell you. Adam and I are thinking about... maybe... moving to Ireland. We thought we'd try it for a year, to see if we like it.'

Suddenly, I'm wide awake. 'Are you? I thought you couldn't. How devastated Adams's parents would be.'

'It's different now Lydia's had her baby. It doesn't mean they won't miss the children, but now they have another grandchild it'll be easier for us to move away.'

'What about Adam's work, your house?'

'Dad said plumbers can always find work. We've given it a lot of thought. We think we can let this house. Letting houses has worked for you. The money we receive will pay the rent on a place in Miltown. I thought you'd be pleased.'

'I am. It's just so sudden. It's taking a while to sink in. Have you told Kate?'

'Not yet. Nor Adam's parents. Now you're here, we wanted your thoughts on it.'

'I'm pleased... surprised... I didn't expect it. I don't think there'll be a problem finding a house to rent. Your dad would love having you nearby.'

'We need to find out what rent we'd get for this house. In the meantime, you can find out what rents are like in Miltown. Have a talk with dad when you get back. Tell him it's only a possibility.'

What can I say? How do I tell her I don't know if I want to stay in Ireland, that there are times when I get close to leaving her father, that our marriage is dead? That the gap between us has grown so wide we've become strangers. That after thirty years of living together I'm still no closer to knowing him. And does he know me? We hardly speak. We avoid each other. Pass like strangers, not touching, keeping our thoughts to ourselves.

Alice and Adam are about to go to the local pub and meet a few friends. I stand in the hallway, waiting for them to leave.

'We'll be back by eleven... We've got our phones... Ring if you need us.'

'That's the second time you've told me that,' I say. 'Just go and enjoy yourselves.'

As soon as I close the door behind them, I go into the lounge. Soft baby sounds are coming through the baby-monitor; a faint tick from the clock. It's eight-thirty – Stella should stay asleep until her next feed; by that time Alice will be back.

I'm hoping Sean won't ring. He was so drunk when I spoke to him last night I sent a prayer of thanks to the miles between us.

This morning I received a call from Diane. I couldn't figure out who it was until she said Sean had given her Alice's telephone number, and I recognised her voice. She wanted to know if she could come to Ireland and stay with us. I told her it wouldn't be a problem. It's then she invited Ella and I to her house for tea.

There's a pile of magazines on the sideboard. I take the one from the top, sit down, open it and flip to the problem page.

Dear Penny, A year ago my husband left me for my best friend. At weekends our two sons stay with them. I feel so lonely when the boys are away. The thought of them playing happy families, with that woman, upsets me. I love my husband and would take him back tomorrow. What can I do? Doreen from Chester.

Dear Doreen, use the weekends to get out and meet new people. There are lots of clubs and organisations that you can join. Ramblers, adult education, volunteering and, if you need them, Samaritans. All will be listed in the telephone directory. Penny.

I think about Doreen and tell myself, if her husband had been happy he wouldn't have left her. Penny's right. She must move on. Find a new life. Still thinking about Doreen, I go into the kitchen, put the kettle on and stand waiting for it to boil, wondering, how could she have been so blind? Didn't she notice her marriage was crumbling and that... The ring of the doorbell alerts me to my own life, to wonder who is at the door. I go to answer it with a mixture of excitement and nerves, a cocktail of desire and reluctance. I open it and hear myself say, 'You've come at the right time; the kettle's just boiled.'

David steps into the house, follows me into the lounge. 'Where is everybody?' he asks.

'They're out with friends. They'll be back any moment. Would you like a drink?'

'A coffee will be nice.'

I leave him and go to the kitchen, pick up the coffee jar and find it empty. As I reach into the cupboard for the unopened jar, a box of cereal falls from the shelf. Cornflakes fly everywhere. I rummage under the sink for the dustpan and brush then kneel on the floor.

I hear David say, 'Can I help?'

'No, I can manage.'

He squats beside me, takes the brush from my hand, sweeps the cornflakes into the dustpan and empties it into the bin. I stand up from the floor.

It feels natural to have his arms around me. As natural as the guilt that makes me say, 'We mustn't. Go into the lounge. I'll bring the coffee when it's ready.'

I put the coffee onto the small table in front of him. Avoiding his gaze, I sit at the other side of the room. Trying to redress the situation, I say, 'Diane rang; she's invited me and Ella to tea. Do you see much of her?'

'Only if I happen to bump into her'.

The conversation stalls and I ask, 'Are you busy?'

A few seconds tick by and he says, 'Will you come to my place tomorrow?'

The excuse rushes from my mouth. 'I'm meeting Liz. I'm helping her choose an outfit for a wedding she's going to.'

'I'll be in all day. Come after you've seen her.'

A faint sound comes through the baby monitor and I jump up, saying, 'Stella's awake. I must go to her.'

I stand at the bottom of the stairs waiting for him to leave. 'I'll see you tomorrow,' he says as he opens the door. The door closing behind him tells me I'll be there. I go into the lounge. The room is silent; his coffee untouched. It's nine-thirty. An hour; that's all it took to untangle the jumble of thoughts in my head, to show me the way I am going.

'You look nice,' says Alice as I come down the stairs. 'I've always liked you in that sweater. You should wear lipstick more often; it suits you.'

She sees me to the door and I go out into the sunshine. 'Have a nice time,' she says. 'Give my love to Liz.'

'I will. Don't cook for me; I'm not sure what time I'll be back. I might go to Liz's after we've finished shopping.'

The bus slows to a crawl as it meets the traffic. It stops at innumerable bus stops and umpteen red traffic lights. I gaze out of the window; so many people. Are they what they appear to be? The severe-looking man hurrying along the busy street, does he hold a secret in his briefcase? The middle-aged woman with down-at-heel shoes, a shoddy coat and bags full of shopping. Is she going home to cook her husband's lunch, or is she in disguise and beneath her shabby clothes something bright and sparkling is happening?

I'm five minutes late when I alight from the bus. Liz waves from across the crowded precinct and we weave our way towards each other.

'Gosh,' she says, 'you look a lot better than when I last saw you. You should wear make-up more often. Do you mind if we have something to eat now? I'm starving.' Taking my arm, she leads me into a large department store where we ride the escalator to the top floor. 'The food's not bad here,' she says, 'and they've some fabulous dresses I'd like you to see.'

We join the queue for food then, carrying our trays, we find an empty table, sit down and she asks, 'How did David's visit go? What's the new girlfriend like?'

'It was fine. The new girlfriend came, but she's not a girlfriend anymore.'

'Same old David, changing women as often as his underpants. Did they have a bust-up while they were with you?'

'No, they'd finished before they came. They're still friends; well, sort of. I think she'd like it to be more.'

'Well, that's David. Easy come, easy go.'

'Yes, that's him,' I say, lifting a chip with my fork and concentrating on the food.

The afternoon is a merry-go-round of fashion floors and make-up counters. Any other time I would have enjoyed it. I look at the clock, hoping that the next pair of shoes will be the right size, the right colour, not too low a heel, not too high, but fashionable! It's gone four when she finds them. 'That's it then,' she says. 'Do you fancy coming to my place?

I've got a casserole in the slow cooker. We can share a bottle or two of wine.'

'I'd rather not. I've a bit of a headache.'

'Oh, that's a shame. Never mind, we'll meet up before you go back. Vicky and Sue are hoping to see you. Give us a ring and we'll see what we can arrange.'

'Yes, I'll do that.' We say goodbye and I watch her disappear into the crowd. Keeping my head down, I leave the shopping precinct and make my way to the waterside building where David lives. I look at the bell to his apartment, still unsure of what I should do. Ignoring the realisation that I'm playing a dangerous game, I press it.

His voice tells me to 'Push the door' and my steps echo from the pale stone floor as I walk past the lift to the stairs. Resting my hand on the stainless steel bannister, I let it lead me to the third floor.

I've only been to his flat once. I try and remember why Sean and I were here. I do remember a girl's embarrassment – she was obviously naked under what must have been David's dressing gown. Clothes were strewn across the floor; her bra was hanging over the back of a chair, his brightly coloured boxer shorts discarded on a black rug.

David is waiting on the landing. He smiles, opens the door to his apartment and I step inside. Papers and magazines are piled on top of chairs. An accumulation of dirty mugs are left on a coffee table.

I hear the door click as it closes behind me. He puts his hand on my shoulder. 'Come into the kitchen; I've wine in the fridge.'

We pass by the bedroom. I notice the king-size bed, the smooth white duvet looking as though it's been freshly laundered for the occasion.

We go into the kitchen. He takes a tea towel from the back of a chair, wipes it, saying, 'Take a seat.' He opens a packet of crisps and pours them into a dish. Moving aside some plates, he puts them onto the table. He takes a bottle of wine from the fridge, pours two glasses and puts one in front of me. All this time I haven't said a word, as though speaking will break the spell and I will be sensible Anna again. I take a sip of wine. The ice-cold liquid gives me courage, and I say, 'I shouldn't be here.'

He stands in front of me, takes my hands, pulls me towards him, and I ask myself, who is this woman, so consumed by desire she is pressing her body to his, enjoying the roughness of his cheek, the smell of his soap...

CHAPTER 11

The familiar sound of urban life wakes me – cars passing by, the clank of a dustbin lid, a woman's Bristol accent shouting at someone to hurry up, Adam's voice calling, 'I won't be long,' the bang of the door – and I open my eyes to a day that shines with possibilities. I look at the clock; I can't believe I've slept so long.

I think about David. We'd been together a good few hours before I began to worry that Alice might ring Liz. I asked him to drive me home. It was about 10.00 p.m. when he parked the car in a quiet back road near where Alice lives. I gave him one last kiss and he said he'd see me soon.

Alice and Adam were watching television when I went into the house. Not wanting to be questioned about my evening, I'd put my head around the door and said, 'Don't let me disturb you. It's been a hectic day and I think I'll go on up to bed.'

Alice immediately stood up and came to the doorway, saying, 'I'm about to make a pot of tea. Would you like one?' Worried she'd see the excitement in my eyes, hear the guilt in my voice, I declined the tea and hurried up the stairs. I went to bed going over every minute spent with David; put my head on my pillow, held it close and fell asleep in his arms.

I get out of bed, look in the mirror and ask myself if this feeling of joy is there for all to see. Trying to compose myself, I put on my plain grey sweater, take the spring from my step and go downstairs.

Ella runs to greet me. 'Nana! We thought you were never going to get up.'

'I'm sorry; I didn't realise it was so late.'

'You said you'd take me to the park.'

'I will. L

How would y(

'Yes,' she s

'Thanks, M

under the stai

tomorrow. Help

and salad stuff in

Stella with you to l

I'm thankful th

pleased Ella and I w

questions that might

'David rang this morning. He said he'll
were coming to tea, but he didn't ta
Diane's words fade behind
David he'd said he'd
I left David he'd
to be this soon!
Diane's compl
meal. He wo
unreliable
She g
be

The door's rendering o

me do it,' she shouts. I l

The tune plays agai   ̣ ̣oor, saying,
'There's no need to rin   ̣ ̣e irritation in her voice
quickly replaced with a smile when she says, 'Come in.'

I put my hand on the pram, saying, 'I hope you don't
mind me bringing Stella. It gives Alice and Adam a bit of
time to themselves; they've a lot to do before tomorrow.'

The smile drops from her face and she says, 'Be careful
not to chip the paint.'

It needs careful manoeuvring to turn the pram in the
tiny box-shaped hall and push it into the spotlessly clean,
neatly furnished, long narrow room. On the G Plan
sideboard is a large cream Persian cat. It stares at us with
huge yellow eyes. Ella puts out her hand and it hisses, leaps
from the sideboard and runs into what looks like a
kitchenette.

'Oscar doesn't like children,' says Diane, following the
cat. I hear a door open and her mutter, 'Poor Oscar; I'll let
you in when they've gone.'

She comes back into the room carrying a white cloth,
and places it over the table. Smoothing it into place, she says,

call in. I told him you
ke the hint. He...'
memories of yesterday. When
see me soon, but I didn't expect it

ants drone on. 'I expect he's after a free
buy a cake but he'll eat mine. He's so
suggest we carry on without him, then he'll...'
es back into the kitchen, her grumbles inaudible
eath the clatter of crockery.

Ella and I sit at the table. 'When are the cakes coming?'
she whispers.

'In a minute,' I say, giving her small hand a squeeze.

Diane carries a tray neatly stacked with a blue and gold
tea set. She puts the tray onto the table then goes back into
the kitchen. I glance around the room. Other than pictures of
cats and their china equivalents, there are no ornaments, no
photographs, no house plants, no pattern on the magnolia
walls. Plain brown curtains hang at the windows, giving a
dark frame to a pristine lawn lorded over by Oscar's yellow
stare and twitching tail.

Diane returns with a cake stand covered with decorated
cupcakes and puts it onto the table. The pink and blue icing,
glazed cherries and silver balls bring a huge smile to Ella's
face.

Suddenly, the cheerful notes of "Waltzing Matilda" fill
the room.

'That's him,' says Diane, going into the hall.

I hear David's voice. My eyes meet his as he comes into
the room. He peers into the pram.

'Is she asleep?' I ask.

He looks up and puts a finger to his lips.

'She's used to noise,' I say.

'Well, in that case...' He leaves the pram, goes to Ella and
tickles her under the chin.

Squealing with laughter, she points to the cakes. 'Look David. Can I have one now, Nana?'

I turn to Diane.

Diane smiles at Ella. 'Take whichever one you like. I'll get the napkins.'

David kisses my cheek. 'How are you?'

This territory is new to me. Yesterday we became lovers; it changed our relationship. It changed my world. Trying to sound as though we hadn't spoken for a while, I say, 'I'm well. What about you?'

'Busy as usual. How's Ireland? How's Sean?' he says, sitting next to me and speaking as though we hadn't seen each other for ages.

I need time to adjust. I'm not comfortable or confident enough to be able to continue this performance. I divert my attention to Ella and the blue icing that's about to spread from her fingers to her pink cotton dress and the white tablecloth. 'Hold on Ella,' I say. 'Let me wipe your hands.' I take the napkin Diane offers me and wipe her fingers, saying, 'We need a damp cloth. Ella, put that cake down a minute.'

Diane fetches a J-cloth, gives it to me and I wipe Ella's fingers. Before she can pick up the cake again I say, 'Let me cut it for you. Try not to get icing everywhere, there's a good girl.' I tuck the napkin under her chin and cut the cake in half.

Diane goes into the kitchen and comes back with a teapot and a glass of squash. She puts the squash next to Ella, sits at the table, puts a cup and saucer in front of her, pours tea and hands it to me. She glares at David. 'Before you start complaining, I'm telling you you're not having it in a mug.' She looks at me. 'He doesn't like a cup and saucer. He thinks they're too fiddley. He actually has his own mug here.' She looks at David. 'You might as well take it back with you. It's cluttering my cupboard.'

He laughs. 'That'll be useful. I've run out. I used the last one this morning. I thought I was going to have to wash up.'

'He's disgusting,' she says. 'You should see the state of his flat. It's filthy. I don't know how he can live in it, and his car's as bad – sweet wrappers all over the floor, rubbish all over the place.'

He winks at Ella. 'We're only here for the cakes, aren't we? We don't mind what we drink from or what state the car's in.'

Laughing, Ella puts her last piece of her cake into her mouth. David picks a pink one covered in silver balls from the cake stand. 'Here, have this one. The icing won't show on your dress.'

Ella looks at me. 'Just one more,' I say.

Diane gives David a look to kill, then asks me, 'What's Sean doing?'

'He's started on the new conservatory, which is one of the reasons he's not here; that and keeping an eye on the garden.'

'I loved Ireland,' she says, looking at David. 'Of course, I would have enjoyed it more if a certain person hadn't been there.'

'You were both in a difficult position.' Feeling her need for reassurance, I say, 'We enjoyed having you. My house must have seemed like a pigsty. How do you manage to keep yours so tidy, bake cakes, and have a full-time job?'

'I enjoy baking. There's not much else to do. Being at work all week doesn't give much time or opportunity to meet people.'

'Do you like your job?'

'No. I sit in an office all day with people I can't stand. When I get home I'm too tired to go out.'

'What about holidays? Do you manage to get away?'

'That's the trouble. As I said, I don't have the opportunity to meet people. The thought of going away by

~ 94 ~

myself... it's not something I'd want to do. I have a week off in November, which is why I got in touch with you.'

'We don't see many people,' I say. 'The weather will probably be terrible, but you're very welcome. It'll be nice to have some company.'

'That's settled then,' she says. 'It'll be the first week in November, if that's okay with you.'

Stella starts to whimper. I stand up, go over to her and take her out of the pram. She looks around the room and lets out a howl. 'I'm sorry about this,' I say, rocking her against my shoulder. 'I expect she's looking for her mum. She's due a feed in about an hour. It's a bit of a walk. We'd better think about leaving.'

David stands up from the table. 'Would you like me to walk back with you?'

I look at Ella – I don't want whispers and secrets darkening my time with her. 'Thanks, but no. I need to pop into the supermarket; Alice asked me to do a bit of shopping.'

Ella looks longingly at the remaining cakes. 'Would you like to take one home?' asks Diane.

Diane puts the cake into a paper bag. I put the baby into the pram.

'I'll give you a ring. It'll be nice to meet up before you go back,' says David as he helps me manoeuvre the pram through the sitting room doorway.

'See you in November,' says Diane as she opens the door.

On the morning of the christening, Kate's early arrival takes us by surprise. 'I thought I'd forego my lie-in and come and give you a hand,' she says, putting her bag onto the floor.

She kisses Ella. 'How's my favourite girl?' She lifts Stella from her baby seat, saying, 'I tried to get your Uncle Sam up, but he doesn't have the same enthusiasm as I have for a party. He's going to meet us at the church.'

'I don't know if you'd call it a party,' I say. 'I think a christening's supposed to be a bit more serious than that.'

'Well, in my role as Godmother I shall encourage her to enjoy life and not take it too seriously.'

'Adam's parents take it seriously,' says Alice as she stacks the breakfast dishes onto the draining board. 'They wouldn't hear of the children not being christened. It was Adam who finally gave in. I think he finds it easier to...'

'What was that?' says Adam, coming into the room.

'I was saying how important christenings are to your mum.'

'They are, and if it makes her happy, why not?'

'Well, Stella's the star of the show,' says Kate holding the baby up for all to see. She turns to look at me. 'It's a shame Dad's not coming.'

'Yes, it is.'

'What have you been up to, Mum? Have you seen your mates? Have you seen David?'

'I helped Liz choose a wedding outfit. I saw David at Diane's yesterday.'

'I thought they weren't together.'

'They're not. What I mean is, they're not a couple but they are friends.'

'He must be hanging around for something. Perhaps she's bridging the gap 'til someone else comes along.'

'We'd better get the quiches out of the freezer,' I say. 'Shall I make a start on the sandwiches?'

After the christening, a dozen of us squeeze into Alice's dining room. I'd been trying to avoid her but it isn't long before I find myself standing next to Adam's mother. We couldn't be more opposite. Me in a bright cotton dress, Elaine in a pale pink suit and cream feathered hat. 'How's life in Ireland?' she asks.

'Fine,' I say, hoping to keep the conversation short.

'I don't know how you can bear being so far away. Bob and I like to be near our family. If they were to move, well, I don't know what we'd do.'

What would she do? Alice thought now Elaine has another grandchild she wouldn't be so upset.

'Your new granddaughter's lovely,' I say. 'Tamsin's such a pretty name. I expect you see a lot of her.'

'We do; we're a close family. We never miss a family get-together. I'm surprised Sean didn't come to the christening.'

'He was sorry not to. He's very busy. Talking of busy, I think I'll start collecting some dishes.' I leave her just in time to avoid Bob as he makes his way towards us.

Kate takes a lipstick from her purse, looks into the mirror, saying, 'We're off in a minute. We're meeting a few friends.'

She puts the lipstick to her lips. Sam smiles at her reflection. 'Come on, Kate; you look gorgeous. If we don't get going soon the night will be over.'

Kate presses her lips together. 'The night's still young.' She kisses his cheek, laughs at the lipstick kiss left there, wipes it away with a tissue, saying, 'Come on. Let's get going.'

Alice collects their jackets from the banister and hands them to Sam. 'Thanks for your help,' she says. 'Your bedtime story worked like magic.'

'We've enjoyed every moment,' says Kate as she slips her jacket on. She turns to look at me. 'When will I see you again?'

I think of David, the little time we have together. 'Um, I...'

'What about Thursday? I'm off that evening. Come for a meal.'

'Kate's working Friday, but I'll take you to the airport,' says Sam as he ushers her to the door.

'I was thinking of asking David. He'd offered to pick me up when I came; I'm sure he won't mind.'

'Okay, but if there's a problem let me know.'

As soon as they leave, Alice, Adam and I go into the lounge. Alice closes her eyes and leans back into her chair. 'Thanks for all your help, Mum.'

The telephone rings and Adam picks it up. 'She's right here. It's David,' he says, passing me the phone.

Holding the phone tight against my ear, I turn my back to Adam as David asks, 'How did the day go?'

'It was great. We're just recovering from the clear-up.'

'What are you doing tomorrow evening?' Do you remember Suzie? I've been invited to a private view at her gallery. Would you like to come?'

I remember Suzie well: flamboyant, attractive – another from David's long list of ex-girlfriends. 'Yes, long dark hair.'

'That's her. Would you like to come?'

'I would.'

'Good, I'll pick you up about seven.'

'I'll look forward to it; see you then.'

No sooner is the phone back in its cradle than it rings again. Adam answers. 'Hello... Is that you, Sean... Yes, she's sitting next to me. You'll have to get in the queue; you're the second bloke to ring her tonight.'

The minute he speaks I know he's drunk. 'Ring when you're sober,' I say. I bang the phone down. 'Sorry,' I tell them. 'It's just... it's just that we've had such a lovely day, and then... and then Sean rings, pissed out of his head!'

The phone rings again. I get up and march to the door. 'Tell him I've gone to bed!'

Hushed murmurs travel around the gallery. I look at the garish paintings trying to make sense of the gaudy clashing colours. We've been here almost an hour. The more I look at the paintings the more I dislike them. Other than David, and a few words to Suzie before she dashed across the room leaving us with – 'Darlings, Joseph Fenwick's here. He's a really important figure in the art world. Help yourselves to drinks.' – I've spoken to no one.

I look across the room. David is in earnest discussion with an expensively dressed middle-aged couple. The debate they are having looks as if it will continue for a while. I open a door that leads to a little veranda and go outside. There's a chill in the air. I wrap my cardigan tightly around myself and look at the view in front of me. The cathedral is floodlit. Lights from the chains of traffic move across the city. I hear the door open and turn to face David.

'What are you doing out here?' he says, putting his arms around me. 'You're cold; come inside.'

I shake my head. 'No, I've nothing to say to those people. I don't understand or like the stuff on those walls. I want to be alone with you. We've such little time left and I can't be late getting back; Alice will wonder where I am.'

He puts his arms around me. His kiss doesn't prevent me hearing the door open. I open my eyes and see Suzie disappear back into the gallery as the door closes behind her.

Panic is in my voice when I say, 'Suzie saw us; she saw us.'

'Don't worry,' laughs David, 'this is the art world. Everybody in there's having an affair of one sort or another.'

This may be the last time I lay in this bed. The last time David and I make love. Tomorrow there will be nothing. I came to him hungry for love, he gave me a taste of honey and the spoon is about to be taken away. I whisper, 'I don't want to go. My marriage is dead.'

'You'll feel differently when you're home. When Alice is there life will be easier. The children will make a huge difference.'

'It won't change my relationship with Sean.'

'You can't say that. You've built a life together.'

'I can say that. Alice, Kate, grandchildren, houses, animals, they haven't brought us together. Sean and I are like strangers.'

He strokes my hair. 'I'll be in touch. I'll visit. We'll find ways, times when we can...'

I kick aside the tangled sheets. Gather my clothes, saying a silent goodbye to the abandoned remains of our love-making – the empty wine glasses next to the bed, his shirt where he'd dropped it on to the black rug, our coffee cups in the sink.

We drive through the city centre, park in a quiet tree-lined street. 'I'll pick you up in the morning,' he says. 'What time did you say your flight is?'

On the long bus journey from Dublin to Ennis I rest my head against the cool thick-paned glass, watching every town, telegraph pole, farm gate and chasing dog flash by.

Thoughts of Alice, Adam and the children moving to Ireland kindle a small spark of hope. They will be here for Sean.

All too soon the bus arrives in Ennis. Within minutes it pulls into the bus station. I spot Sean. He looks up, puts his cigarette butt into a bin, waits for me to alight and says, 'I'll get your cases.'

We don't touch. There's no brush of cheeks. No excitement in his eyes – nothing to make me want to be with him.

CHAPTER 12

The bumpy ride down the lane brings my journey to its end. Sean turns off the engine and for a moment we sit in silence. The sun is beginning to fall behind the barn, the last of its rays catching the brilliant oranges, reds and yellows of a patch of nasturtiums. Blackie is in his usual place by the barn. He stands when Sean gets out of the car. His ears prick when I open the passenger door; he runs towards me, rolls onto his back and I bend to rub his belly.

Sean carries my case into the house. I collect my coat from the back seat. Blackie is racing around the yard with the energy of a puppy. Frantically wagging his tail, he runs towards me. I bend over and he licks my face, filling the air with his doggy breath. I fondle the rough fur around his neck. Stroking his silky ears, I look into his trusting eyes and whisper, 'I'm sorry, but I'm going to have to let you down.'

Sean calls, 'I've made tea; it's on the table.'

I look at the house with dread, a feeling that the building will gobble me up, swallow me whole.

I put my coat and bag into the porch, walk around the side of the house and stand with my back to the conservatory Sean has started to build.

I look at the view that brought such hope. The same stone walls criss-cross the never-ending shades of green. The same scraggy pines grow in untidy clumps on the western side of the garden. If I stand amongst them I'll catch sight of the Kerry mountains before they disappear with the sunset. There's a hush across the valley. The cattle have been put to bed. Lights shine from cottage windows. Martins scoop a cloud of midges before flying to their nests.

Ireland hasn't changed, neither has Sean. I'm the one who sees things differently. Living here has shown me as clearly as if it were written on the distant hills that my love for Sean means no more to him than a cosy jacket, or a well-worn pair of slippers. Well, they are both about to be taken away.

Night falls. A small movement catches my eye. A little mouse has poked her nose out of a crack in the dry stone wall. She moves stealthily down the wall onto the patio. She hasn't seen Blackie and I, or Lily hiding in the undergrowth. Lily jumps. The mouse darts across the flagstones and disappears beneath a fuchsia bush. A light from the kitchen window, a note from the fiddle, tells me I cannot hide here forever.

I collect my jacket and bag from the porch and go into the house. Sean puts his fiddle down. 'What have you been doing? The tea's cold. Are you hungry? There's a beef stew on the hob.'

'I've been sitting outside.'

'In the dark?'

'Yes.'

I go to the stove and ladle a spoonful of stew into a bowl. 'I've something to tell you,' I say as I take the bowl to the table. 'Alice and Adam are thinking about moving to Miltown. They said they'll give it a year to see if they like it.'

He looks at me with surprise. 'I thought they'd said they couldn't because... What's Adam's mum's name?'

'Elaine. Alice thinks that now Lydia has a baby it won't be such a wrench.'

'Where are they going to live, and what are they going to live on?'

'They'll let their house and rent one in Miltown, You've said yourself plumbers can always get work.'

'It comes as a bit of a surprise, but it'll be great to have them around. How are our tenants? Did you see them?'

'No, I didn't.'

'Why not? I thought that was one of the reasons for going.'

'Time flew by. What with the christening and everything, it was time to leave before I knew it.' I pick up my bowl, empty the stew back into the saucepan saying, 'I'm sorry, I'm not hungry. I might have some later. I'm going to unpack.' Sean picks up his fiddle and a slow air follows me up the stairs.

It's been three days since I left Bristol; it feels like three weeks. Trying to avoid Sean as much as I can, I'm in the garden whatever the weather, out walking with Bridie most days. I slope off to bed as early as possible, keeping strictly to my side, feigning sleep when Sean gets in beside me.

I've heard nothing from David.

It's been five days since I left Bristol. I've left five messages on David's answering machine and haven't heard a word from him.

It's 6.00 a.m. and I'm in the kitchen wondering whether I should drive to Miltown, go to the phone box and ring David. Sean was drinking heavily last night. I convince myself he won't wake up until late morning.

The phone box is littered with dog-ends; there's a strong smell of urine. Pushing back the feeling of nausea, I pick up the receiver, dial David's number and feed in a handful of coins. The message I leave is always the same: 'I need to speak to you. Call early morning when Sean's asleep.'

I leave the phone box and hurry to the newsagent. Clutching the writing paper and envelopes I've bought I get back into the car and drive to the church car park. As I expected, the car park is deserted. Other than the church, there is no other building in sight. Safe from prying eyes, I take a pen from my bag.

Dear David,

I miss you very much. It's frustrating not being able to talk to you. There are so many things I want to say. I think of you every minute of the day.

Do you get my messages? The disappointment when you don't answer is overwhelming. I tell myself you must be busy. When is a good time to ring? I need to hear your voice desperately.

I hate being here, not being able to see you casts a cloud over every day whatever the weather, though it may not be for much longer.

I have found a house for Alice. I saw the advertisement in a shop window the day after I arrived back. I rang and viewed it that same day. It's a very pleasant three-bedroomed bungalow on the edge of town. It's furnished, which is what they want. Alice and Adam said it sounds ideal and, as they're only waiting for references from a prospective tenant, I put a deposit down. So, it may be only a month or two before we're together again.

I will wait until Alice and family are settled before I say or do anything. Sean will be fine with them here to support him. To be honest, what little he and I had is gone. Who knows? It might give him the chance to find someone who will make him happy.

Please ring. I know we won't be able to say the things we long to hear, but just to hear your voice, to know you're well will make things easier for me.

I send you all my love.

Yours forever,

Anna x

I kiss the letter and tuck it into the envelope. Writing the words, knowing that in a few days David will read them, brings him a little closer. I get out of the car and walk to the post-office. The letter falls into the post box. If only I could arrive at his door as quickly and easily.

I tackle brambles and weeds like a demon. It's been four days since I posted the letter. A few weeks ago our passion overrode all sense of right or wrong. The times we spent together were electric. I can't believe his feelings have changed.

Thirst makes me look towards the house. Not wanting to cross paths with Sean, I carry on with the brambles. The phone rings and stops. My heart jumps with the thought that it might be David and I put down my tools. I hurry to the house, go into the kitchen and hear Sean say, 'Yes, it's coming along nicely... I haven't decided about windows... I'll probably go for double glazing.'

Listening to Sean, I go to the sink and fill a glass with water.

'There's a glazier in Ennis. I'll give him a try first. Anyway, how are things with you?'

I sit at the table sipping the water, wondering if it is David he's talking to – Sean would never talk to his dad about building, and Adam wouldn't ring him at this time of day.

'Bloody hell, that's daylight robbery... Try another garage. You haven't had that car five minutes. What have you been doing to bugger it up like that? ...Yes, she's just come.'

I'm getting ready to stand when Sean says, 'Do you still see Derek? He was always good with engines.'

I have the urge to tear the phone from Sean's hand.

'You know Derek, the little ginger bloke that used to do a spot of plastering from time to time. You might find him in the phone book; unusual name, Becket, or something like that... Yes, she's here. Do you want a word with her?... It's David.'

I stand up and take the phone, turn my back my back to Sean and gaze out of the window.

'Morning, Anna. How are you?'

His voice is as casual, as cheerful as greeting a neighbour. 'Okay,' I say, wondering if he's received my letter.

'How was your journey home?'

I turn back towards the kitchen. Sean is sat at the table changing a fiddle string. 'As I expected, long and tiring. Has Sean told you Alice and Adam are thinking about moving to Miltown?'

'Yes, I rang yesterday.'

'Did you?' – Sean never told me David rang but why would he, Sean and I hardly speak to each other.

'I received your letter, Anna. Don't do anything rash. Things will be easier when Alice and the family are with you.'

'Yes, it will be easier.'

'Good, I'm glad you feel that way.' – Does David understand the implications of my words?

Close to saying something I might regret, I quickly tell him, 'I must go. It looks as though it's going to rain and I've left my tools in the garden.'

'Yes, so must I. Take care.'

The opportunity to speak openly to him disappears like water into vapour. I put the phone down. Sean looks up from his task. 'What do you mean? What will be easier?'

'When Alice and the children are here, we... I... you won't be lonely.'

CHAPTER 13

'Mum! We've received the references. The tenants want to move in as soon as possible. It won't be long before we're with you.'

Alice's voice is like music; suddenly the world is a brighter place. 'That's good news. When are they moving in? When do you think you'll be here?'

'It could be a matter of weeks.'

'Weeks! That's great!'

'Adam has a few jobs to finish, but there's nothing to prevent me and the children leaving as soon as we're packed and ready. Kate said, if he needs to, Adam can stay with them. I'll bring a few things. He can bring the rest when he joins us. Ella's already packed. She's so funny. She's put her swimming costume, rubber ring, bucket, spade and doll into her doll's pram and parked it by the front door so we won't forget it! Adam's mum and dad aren't happy. I told them we'll be fine, that Ella will make lots of friends at school, which reminds me, will you call in and enrol her?'

'Yes, I'll do that tomorrow.'

'Do you mind having another look at the house? Check it has all we need?'

'I'll look in after I've been to the school. You know you can stay with us for as long as you like. There might be a few things to do in the house. You don't have to dash off straight away.'

'Thanks, that's good to know. Can you get Dad to have a look at the boiler?'

'Why don't you ask him yourself?'

I give the phone to Sean. 'I'm going into town,' I say, picking up my car keys.

I'm hopeful, ever hopeful that David will pick up the phone, though it doesn't surprise me when the automated voice says he's unavailable and I've only enough time to leave one garbled message, scant with missing words.

Ready armed with paper and pen, I hurry a letter, rush to the post box, only to see the post van drive away. I push the letter into the empty box, walk to the car with worries and concerns circling my thoughts like sharks – When do I tell Alice? What will Kate think? How will Sean manage without me? – The enormity of what I'm about to do pulls like a magnet, leaves me powerless to want anything other than being with David.

If it wasn't for the tick of the clock, the house would be as quiet as a church. I glance out of the window. Sean is sat on the stone wall staring into the distance. Hoping he will stay that way, I quickly gather together the utensils and ingredients to make pasties.

The mixing bowl and rolling pin has been washed and put away. The aroma of pastry, herbs and beef wafts from the oven. I'm about to go and check on the pasties when I hear Sean come into the room. I look down at the cookery book on my lap. Sean stops beside me. If I move my eyes just a fraction from the page I will see his boots, the frayed edge of his jeans.

'Anna?' His voice is soft. 'What's the matter? Tell me what's wrong?'

I stare at the page, the letters swim in my tears.

'Don't you like it here? We'll move away if you're unhappy.'

I daren't look up, don't want him to see the tear making a slow journey down the contour of my face. Don't want to look at him through a water veil that may soften his edges.

'Anna, please.'

His kind words put a chink in my armour, touch a sleeping seed. I shake my head, not daring to look at him.

'FOR CHRIST'S SAKE, WHAT AM I TO DO?' Anger spins around the room. A cup, a plate shatter on the tiled floor. The door opens and slams. The car's engine roars into life and fades into the distance.

I don't remember taking the pasties from the oven, or clearing the broken crockery from the floor. I must have been sat at the table for quite a while – the light from the window is beginning to fade. I look at the clock – Bridie will be waiting for me.

I put one pasty on a plate for Sean. The rest I pack into the freezer, on top of the growing amount of Sean's favourite food.

Bridie is standing at her sitting-room window. She sees me and within seconds she's walking down her path, fastening the brass buttons on her navy blazer. 'That dog loves you,' she says as she closes the gate.

I look down at Blackie. 'I've grown very fond of him.' Blinking back a tear, I look up, saying, 'Where shall we go?'

'Let's go to the lake.' She starts to tell me about a nephew's forthcoming wedding. I'm half listening, my mind elsewhere, wondering how many more times Bridie and I will go walking together, if this will be the last time I stand at the edge of the lake, the last time l hear the skylark's song, the last time I see the moor mauve with heather. I want to tell Bridie everything that's happening in my life but couldn't bear her disapproval. She will disapprove, there's no doubt about it. Bridie believes marriage is for better or worse. She takes her religion seriously – three masses every weekend, a pilgrimage to Knock twice a year. I envy the smooth, unrumpled whiteness of Bridie's life. If only I could believe in her God. If only it were enough. Bridie's voice breaks my thoughts. 'We should head back; it'll be dark soon.'

We stop at the top of the lane and I look down at the house – the kitchen light is on – Sean must be home. I want to ask Bridie how I can find her God. How to accept what life has given me. But there's a primeval force older than Aphrodite that makes me turn away and say goodnight.

Sean's head is on the table, his eyes are closed. The remnant of pasty litters the floor. Silently, I go up to the bedroom.

I lie awake for what seems like hours. Turn my face to the wall when I hear Sean on the stairs. He comes into the room. His body falls across me and I breathe in the smell of beer and wine. Pushing him away, I spring from the bed shouting, 'Don't touch me!' The room is pitch black but it only takes a second to realise he's unconscious. Alcohol is a far more agreeable companion than I am.

Sean and I are wrapped in our own worlds. I don't know what's happening in his but mine is preparation. The garden is weed-free, the house spotless, there are enough vegetables to last Sean and Alice well into the winter.

Alice will be here in a few days. I still don't know how and when to tell her I'm leaving. I've spoken to David. It was such a relief to hear his voice. I was disappointed but not surprised when he tried to persuade me to stay where I am. I reminded him how wonderful our love-making was, that we made love like only people who care deeply for each other can. He said he didn't want to break my relationship with Sean. I told him it broke a long time ago. Once again, he said things will improve when Alice is with me. I didn't answer. He made me promise to keep our relationship a secret. I told myself that when I'm free the whole world will know I am his.

Sean's tail lights disappear at the top of the lane. In less than two hours he'll be back with Alice and the children. I pick up the phone and dial David's number. I leave no message.

The desire to talk to someone who will understand and support me is overwhelming. I remember lunch breaks, endless cups of coffee, a quick visit to a wine bar before going home. Vicky, upset because of Craig's latest liaison, me in tears over a broken night's sleep wondering if Sean was lying drunk in a gutter. We supplied each other with tissues, hugged and laughed at what we called our mutual support group.

Vicky answers the phone almost immediately.

'Vicky, it's Anna.'

'Hi, nice to hear you. How are you?'

I jump the nicety of polite conversation. 'I'm leaving Sean.'

'You're what!'

'Leaving; I'm leaving Sean.'

'Why? What's happened?'

'It's his drinking. I can't put up with it any longer. For years I've...'

'You've put up with it for years. So why now?'

'Because... because... it's different here.'

'There's someone else...'

'It's harder here, just the two of us. Sean's drinking is out of control.'

'Who is it, Anna?'

'If you must know, it's David.'

'For God's sake! Not David! What does Alice think? She's going over to live near you, isn't she?'

'Yes; Sean's collecting them from the airport now.'

'Well, what does she think? You have told her, haven't you? She does know?'

'No, she doesn't. I haven't...'

'You haven't! Anna! The girl's moving to Ireland, bringing your grandchildren! Have you lost your senses?'

'Perhaps I have. If I'd told her she might not have come. I would never have been able to leave; never had a chance of happiness.'

'Anna, I know more than anyone how difficult your marriage has been. We've supported each other through some pretty difficult times but things change. Craig and I... well, we've reached a kind of truce. It'll be better when Alice is with you. You can't do this to her, and not with David. He's Sean's friend! Please Anna. Give it a while. Wait and see how...'

'I've given it thirty years.' My voice rises with frustration. 'Alice has to be here. Sean won't survive by himself. I can't help who I fall in love with!'

Vicky's tone softens. 'Be careful, Anna.'

'I will. Goodnight.'

I think about Alice. How will I tell her, and what about Kate – she adores her father. Will they believe me when I tell them I left because of Sean's drinking and that it had nothing to do with David.

I look at the table, at the freshly picked lettuce and nasturtiums in the willow patterned bowl, the homemade bread, the mussels gathered from rocks wet from the receding tide, the jug of wild flowers and honeysuckle... a honey trap for Alice?

The sound of the car's engine, the headlights turning the yellow curtains to a beacon, moves me to the door. I go to the car and take Stella from Alice's arms. 'It's good to see you, Mum,' she says. 'Here at last.' She gets out of the car. Sean lifts a sleeping Ella from the back seat.

'You must all be tired,' I say.

'We are. It's been a long day. We had a two-hour wait in Dublin Airport.'

We go into the house. Still half asleep, Ella gazes around the room then, seeing her mother, she holds out her arms. Alice takes her from Sean and looks at the table. 'Ella's had plenty of snacks on the journey; she won't be hungry. I'll get her ready for bed.'

I take Stella into the sitting room, pleased to be left on my own with the sleeping baby. I listen to Sean bringing in the cases, his and Alice's voices.

Alice opens the sitting room door. 'Would you like to say goodnight to Ella?'

'Yes, of course.' I'm aware of the puzzled expression on Alice's face as she takes Stella from my arms.

'Are you all right?' she asks.

'Yes, I'm fine. I'll say goodnight to Ella then I'll put the mussels on. Supper won't be long.'

Neither the flowers nor the food brighten the atmosphere. I make light conversation by relating a few bits of gossip I've heard in town but it falls flat. Sean and I barely look at each other. It isn't until Alice tells us Adam hopes to join them in about two weeks that Sean shows the faintest interest in what's being said. I'm glad when the meal is over and Alice says she needs to go to bed. It gives me the excuse to do the same.

Last night's gloom is lifted by Ella's excited chatter. It brings a smile, even to the likes of me and Sean. She's still in her pyjamas when she dashes out to see Blackie and comes back inside saying, 'Nana, can Blackie come and see my new house with us?'

'No, he has to stay here.'

'When are we going to my new house?'

'After we've had breakfast and cleared up. Now sit at the table.'

'Please can Blackie come?'

'No, Blackie doesn't like being away from home.'

'Granddad, can Blackie come to my house?'

'No, Blackie belongs here. He'll get lost if he goes anywhere else.'

'Mummy, can I have a dog?'

'Maybe sometime but not now.'

'Daddy will let me have one.'

'You can come and see Blackie whenever you like,' I say, putting a bowl of cereal in front of her.

'When we move into our house, can I come and take him for walks with you, Nana?'

Guilt comes with a crash. 'Ella! If you don't hurry up and eat your breakfast we'll never get to your house!' Her chin quivers as she picks up her spoon. Tears fill her eyes.

'Don't shout at her. What's wrong with you, Anna?' asks Sean.

I look at Ella. 'I'm sorry. You can come whenever you like, though it'll probably be Blackie taking you for a walk, not you taking Blackie!'

Alice comes into the kitchen carrying Stella. 'What's the matter, Mum? Is everything all right?'

'Yes, I'm sorry. I shouldn't have shouted. Ella's done nothing wrong. I've a headache.'

I'm angry with myself for upsetting Ella. It won't happen again. I'll spend these few weeks helping Alice settle into Miltown. I won't spoil them by telling her I'm leaving. I'll wait until Adam arrives. She'll come to understand, so will Kate, that Sean and I will be happier apart.

'Look, Ella,' I say, holding her up so she can see over the drystone wall. 'Meet your neighbours.' A group of cows lift their heads from chewing grass and stare at us. 'Now let them finish their dinner while we go into your new house.'

Sean has brought the last of Alice's cases which, together with the bags and Stella's buggy, take up most of the floor space in the hallway. We go into the kitchen. Alice is searching through a rucksack full of baby paraphernalia. She looks up at us. 'It's a great house, Mum. Thanks for finding it.'

'There's cows outside,' shouts Ella, jumping up and down. 'Can I take them for a walk? Nana said the beach is down the end of the road. Can we take them there?'

'No,' laughs Alice. 'The cows stay in the field and there are things we need to do before we go to the beach.'

'When you're ready, I'll take you shopping,' I say.

'That'll be good. I'll change Stella and then we can go.'

'Is there anything I can do?' asks Sean.

'No,' is my quick reply. 'We can manage.'

'In that case, I'll...'

'Wait here, Dad; we won't be long. I'll make us tea when we get back.'

'I'd better be going. I need to finish a few things on the house...' He looks at me. I can see he's waiting to be talked into staying.

'We don't want too many cooks,' I say.

'Well, I'll be off then.'

Alice kisses his cheek. 'Thanks for everything, Dad. It's great having you and Mum nearby.'

Alice and I spend a few hours shopping and unpacking. Ella is eager to go to the beach. After we've eaten, we push Stella in her buggy and play on the sand. It's gone 7.00 p.m. when I help Alice put the children to bed.

The following morning, I wake with a sense of relief, pleased to have an excuse to get out of the house. I'm about to leave when Sean comes down the stairs. I look up at him as I put my jacket on. 'I'm going to Alice's. There are a couple of boiled eggs and the coffee's still warm.'

'I won't be seeing you at all soon. Next thing, you'll be moving in with them. Couldn't wait to find a place for them, could you?'

'She needs our help at the moment. There could come a time when we might need her.'

Alice has been in Miltown for over a week. Our daily visits to each other have made life a little more bearable. Oddly, there's been a marked change in Sean's behaviour. He's been very attentive, brings me drinks when I'm working in the garden, takes an interest in what I'm doing. His alcohol consumption has dropped; in fact, a half bottle of wine has been left on the dresser – something I've never known happen before.

Today he insisted on preparing and cooking a Sunday roast for us all. When Alice and the children left, we sat and watched television together – a rare event.

His behaviour feels strange. It's too sudden. I like it but it makes me nervous.

'I didn't know you were such a good cook,' I say. 'Thank you for a lovely meal. You must invite them to dinner again.'

I pick up my empty cup. 'I'm off to bed.'

'I'll watch the end of this programme and join you.'

I lie in bed thinking about the day. It was the sort of Sunday I imagine other families enjoy. The sort of Sunday I've wanted and envied. I hear Sean climb the stairs, listen as he undresses and gets into bed. He whispers my name, strokes my arm and I hold myself still. The seconds tick by... Suddenly he throws the cover aside, gets out of bed, shouting, 'FUCK YOU, ANNA! IF THAT'S WHAT YOU WANT, WE'LL SPEND THE REST OF OUR LIVES NOT TALKING TO EACH OTHER!' Cursing and swearing, he puts on his dressing gown, leaving the room with a bang of the door.

Something delicate and fragile has slipped through my fingers and I don't trust him enough to look for the pieces.

Early morning light creeps through the weave of the curtain. I am wearing black leather shoes and my best black coat. In my hand is a small brown suitcase.

Sean is lying on the sofa. His eyes are open. Lily is asleep on his chest.

'I'm leaving.'

His eyes are focused on the ceiling. 'Fuck off then.'

The force of his words turns me around, moves me from the room. I take the car keys from the dresser, open the door and go outside. It's raining. Blackie's wet nose sniffs my hand. I get into the car and drive out of the yard.

I park outside Alice's bungalow. She answers the door. 'What on earth's the matter?'

'I'm leaving your father.'

'Leaving?' she looks at the suitcase. 'Where are you going? What's he done? Come in out of the rain.'

Ella touches my hand. 'Nana?'

'Leave Nana alone for a minute. I'll put the kettle on. Tell me what's happened?'

'I'm not stopping. I must go. Your father and I... We haven't... I've had enough. I can't live with him anymore.' I put my car keys into Alice's hand. 'Give these to him. His car isn't reliable. He'll need mine more than I do.'

Ella watches from her bedroom door, her mouth open, confusion in her eyes. The baby starts to cry.

'Wait, stay a minute,' says Alice as she hurries into the sitting room. She comes back holding Stella against her shoulder. 'Don't stand outside. Where are you going?'

'I won't come in. I'm going to Bristol.'

'Bristol! Why? What's Dad done?'

'His drinking – I've had enough. I need to get away.'

'Dad's always liked a drink. Why now?' Alice smiles; it is a smile of realisation. 'I know. There's someone else. Tell me the truth. There's someone else!'

Alice screams, and the children's cries pursue me as I run down the path.

CHAPTER 14

I step from the hotel's revolving door onto the plush red carpet. A group of smartly dressed people are queuing at the reception desk. They turn to look at me – their welcoming smiles quickly replaced by furtive glances and whispers. The slow trickle of rainwater down the back of my neck makes me aware of how I must look. My woollen coat is sodden, my feet swimming in the black leather court shoes; the small brown suitcase's shabbiness exposed for all to see.

I look for a phone. Not seeing one, I join the queue for reception. The young couple in front of me shift uncomfortably forward, making a space between them and the wet stranger. As I move closer to reception, my reflection in a large gilt-framed mirror comes into view. My eyes are red from crying. The rain has flattened my hair and I see the drip, drip from a loose tendril.

'Can I help you?' The receptionist's lip-glossed red mouth is without warmth or expression.

'Do you have a phone I can use? I need to call a taxi.'

Her pale blue eyes stare at me beneath a polished coal black fringe. 'You'll have to use the call box.'

'Where is it?'

'In the bar.'

'Do you have a taxi number?'

She purses her lips and deep cracks appear in the crimson gloss. 'No, I haven't.' She takes a deep breath. 'Can't you see I'm busy? You'll have to ask the barman.'

I leave her and push my way through the newly arrived guests. A few couples slowly make their way to the lounge. I hurry past them and head for the bar. The elderly barman is pulling a pint of Guinness. He places the almost full glass next to three others then one by one puts them back under the pump, filling each one to the brim and putting them on the counter in front of a large man with a loud American accent. The American pays for the drinks, saying, 'I've been waiting for this. It's a long way to come for a Guinness, but worth every mile.' He picks up two of the pints and the barman turns towards me.

'What can I get you?' The creases around his eyes have left the marks of a merry life.

Relieved to find a friendly face, I say, 'I need to call a taxi. The receptionist said you'll have a number?'

'I'll give you my neighbour's number. He's very reliable.'

He goes to the till and picks up a pad and pen, is on his way back to me when the American returns, looks at the barman and says, 'Do you know a Tom Kelly living round here?'

The barman turns to him and says, 'There's a Tom Kelly in Mullagh. He has a small dairy farm. His family have farmed that land for generations.'

'Hey, that might be the Tom Kelly I'm looking for. Where's Mullagh?'

The barman goes over to the American and puts the pad onto the counter. 'I'll draw you a map.'

My taxi retreats into the distance as I listen to the barman explaining how to get to Tom's farm. Finally, the American puts the map into his pocket, picks up the remaining two pints, saying, 'That's great. Thanks a lot.'

The barman comes towards me. 'Now, Luke's number.' He writes the number down, hands it to me and points across the room. 'The phone's in the corner.'

I'm about to leave the bar when I remember I've only got notes and say, 'Can you give me some change?'

'Hang on,' says the barman. 'I'll just serve this customer.'

I glance around, worried that someone might recognise me, that someone I know will walk through the door and wonder why I'm here. After what feels like a lifetime, the barman exchanges my note for coins and I hurry to the phone.

Luke said he'd be here in five minutes. Already nine have disappeared. When I see headlights and the lit taxi sign I leave the shelter of the hotel and go outside. Luke rolls down the car window, asking, 'Are you for Ennis?' His face is familiar. He gets out of the car, takes my case and I climb into the back seat. When he gets back into the car he turns to look at me. 'You're Sean's wife. I'm Tom's brother. Your neighbour! I'm his brother.'

I don't reply – like Sean, I thought I'd be anonymous in the hotel, go unnoticed amongst the holiday-makers.

'I've driven Sean home many times,' says Luke as he drives away. 'He sure likes his drink. Fell out the car a few times when we got to your place. Though I always made sure he was able to stand up and get inside. I haven't seen him about for a while...'

Luke ignores my silence. His voice becomes one with the engine's drone, his words meaningless.

'Why are you going to Ennis?'

His question invades my thoughts.

'Why are you going to Ennis?' he persists.

'I had an urgent call. A friend in England is seriously ill. I'm getting the early train to Dublin.'

'Have you booked anywhere to stay tonight?'

'No. I'll find somewhere.'

'My cousin Edna runs a B&B. She makes a grand Irish breakfast. I'll drop you there if you like? If she's booked we'll find somewhere else.'

His words disappear with the passing landscape. It isn't until we stop outside a large pebble-dashed bungalow with a neat garden that I realise we're in Ennis.

Luke leaves the car, walks up the garden path and stands talking to a woman at the door. He comes back smiling and I get out of the car. He takes my case from the boot, saying, 'I'll carry it into the house for you.'

'It's not heavy; I can manage.'

He hesitates before giving it to me and asks, 'Are you all right?'

I force a smile. 'Yes, I'm fine.'

'Edna's a grand one for listening,' he says as he gives me my case. 'She'll look after you. If you need anything, she'll...'

'Please don't worry about me.'

Going back to the car, he turns to me and says, 'Take care. God bless you.'

The garden gate is open. Edna is waiting in the doorway. Alice's screams and Ella's cry follow me along a path bordered with the russet colours of chrysanthemums.

Edna smiles a welcome and I step into the house. A large golden Labrador lies across the hallway. 'Mind yourself, Goldie,' says Edna nudging him with her foot. Goldie lifts his heavy bulk from the thick-piled brown carpet and we follow him into a comfortably furnished sitting room.

'How long will you be staying? I charge fifteen punts a night. Does that suit?' asks Edna.

'I'll be here one night. Fifteen punts is fine.'

'Luke said you're visiting a sick friend. I hope it's not serious.'

'Serious enough for me to go to England but she'll improve.'

'Sit down. Make yourself comfortable while I get your room ready. Would you like a cup of tea?'

'No, thank you. I need to make a phone call. Where's the nearest phone box?'

'Turn right at the end of the road. You can't miss it... Hang on! Let me give you a key.'

'Anna, is that you? Why are you crying? What's happened?'

I take a deep breath. 'David, I've left Sean.'

'You've what! Anna! Stop crying!'

'Sorry... I'm so sorry.'

'Stop saying sorry, and tell me what happened.'

'I couldn't stay any longer. I had to go.'

'Go where?'

'To you, to Bristol.'

'What about Alice? Have you spoken to her?'

'Yes, I left the car with her.'

'What did she say? What does she think?'

'I don't care what she thinks. I'm flying to Bristol tomorrow.'

'Where are you now?'

'In Ennis.'

'Anna, it's not too late. Go home.'

'I'm not going back. I want to be with you.'

'Can't you see? Life's not that simple. It's not that easy. What will everyone think? You can't just walk away. They'll worry about you.'

'David! Please be at the airport. The plane will arrive at five-fifteen. Please be there.'

'Okay. I'll be there. We'll talk about it then.'

Relief washes over me. 'Thank you, thank you.'

As soon as I enter the house, Edna greets me with an offer of tea and cake. I make the excuse of a headache and go to my room.

Tiredness overtakes me and I fall into a dream – a delicate moment slipping through my fingers; harsh words, an abandoned black and white collie, a child crying. The house is dark and silent when I put fifteen punts and the key onto the hall table, when I nudge the dog from his place in front of the door.

Train doors open and slam. Fields, trees, houses appear and disappear. Everything wiped away by speed and time. My credit card, my passport open the door to the departure lounge. I follow the sea with the eye of a gull. Shadows sweep across the green, green grass of Wales. Rooftops swell, lanes become roads, toys become cars. Bristol's runway widens, widens, widens.

I'm amongst the first to leave the plane. I hurry past the people in front of me, winning the race to retrieve luggage. Flight R125 flashes above a motionless carousel. I go to the toilets and look in the mirror. The reflection is unwelcome. My hair, left to dry in a tangle, tugs against the comb. I apply blusher and lipstick to a pale face.

The rattle from the carousel quickens my step. The brown suitcase, small and scruffy, easily identified. I grab it and hurry into the terminal. David isn't here. I look at the clock; the plane was five minutes early.

People begin to congregate. I watch the raptured greetings of families, friends and lovers. The kisses, hugs and smiles. I listen to laughter, exclamations of joy. They leave hand in hand, arm in arm, carrying cases and bags, gifts – CDs of Daniel O'Donnell, fluffy leprechauns, toy whistles, Burren smoked salmon. I watch until the last one disappears through the exit.

I worry he may not come, then the automatic door opens and I see him. His face is serious. He hurries towards me and picks up my case, saying, 'The best thing to do is take you to Kate's.'

'No! They won't be there. They're always out. I need to speak to her first.'

'Where can I take you?'

'To your place.'

'You can't. What will everyone think? What about Sean? Your girls? It'll destroy your relationships. How about one of your friends? What about Vicky? She'll put you up until you sort yourself out.'

'I can't; Craig won't want me there. I know what he's like. It'll only cause trouble.'

'What about Liz, or Sue? They live on their own. You can stay with one of them.'

'NO!' I stifle a sob. David looks around – people are beginning to look at us.

'Okay. We'll go to my place. We'll talk there.' He takes my arm and hurries me out of the building.

The last time I was in David's car is so very different from now – his hand no longer touches my knee; the constant looks and smiles have disappeared. 'I know it's hard for you,' I say, 'Sean being your...'

'You shouldn't have run off like that. Things would have improved with Alice being there.'

'I had to. I couldn't stay any longer.'

'You should have given it time.'

'Alice being there wouldn't change things. My love for Sean has gone. I love you. I thought you cared.'

'I do, but you're Sean's wife. What we did. Well, it happened and you're here now.'

He pulls into the underground car park of his apartment and I follow him up the stairs.

The apartment is as cheerless as David's greeting. He pulls a curtain aside and a glimmer of light falls onto the cluttered room. I move a pile of magazines from a chair and sit down, remembering the first time we made love. He had been gentle and caring. I thought he felt the same way as I did.

He puts a mug of tea in front of me and walks to the window. Leaving the tea, I stand beside him.

Night is falling. The sound of laughter travels across the river. Coloured lights blink and dance on the surface of the water.

I touch his shoulder. 'David, please don't be angry.' I put my arms around him and he pushes me to the floor. I help him remove my clothes. He enters me and our love-making is quickly over. When he stands, I look up at him. 'I've work to do,' he says. 'There's bread and cheese if you're hungry. You know where the bed is. We'll talk in the morning.'

I lie in bed, bewildered by his coldness. I listen to the sound of people enjoying themselves, the farewells, the occasional drunken call.

It must be well past midnight when David gets into bed. I put my arm around him. He turns away.

When I wake, I put out my hand to touch him and find an empty space. I wrap myself in his dressing-gown and follow the smell of coffee to the kitchen. He looks up at me. 'I've been thinking,' he says. 'It's best you don't stay here. My sister lives a couple of miles from here. She has a spare room. I'll tell her you're a friend and that you need a place to stay until you get yourself sorted.'

David had never mentioned a sister. There's so much I don't know about him. I shake my head. 'I want to stay here.'

'I've told you, you can't, which is why I'm taking you to Eve's.'

'She might not want me. What about her husband?'

'She's not married. She'll be glad of the company.' He stands up and puts his cup with the pile of dishes in the sink. 'Get yourself ready. I'm going to take you to Eve's now. Nobody knows what happened between us. You haven't told anybody have you?'

I think back to the telephone call I had with Vicky. 'Vicky rang me a few weeks back. I told her I was leaving Sean. I didn't say anything about you but she guessed. I'm sorry, I'm sure she won't say any...'

'For Christ's sake, now everybody will know.'

'Vicky's my friend. She won't...'

'Dammit! I'll ring Eve now. The quicker you're out of here the better.'

CHAPTER 15

Eve closes the door and turns to look at me. There's no hiding the look of disappointment on her face. David had been here less than five minutes when he gave her a quick peck on the cheek and said he had to dash. She gives me a shy smile and says, 'Let me show you your room.'

She's a bird-like woman, small and thin with steel grey hair, her bi-focal glasses much too large for her face – which must have been quite delicate and pretty when she was younger. Instead of giving her the look of an owl, the glasses reduce her to that of a nervous wren. She looks at my case and asks, 'Is that the only luggage?'

'Yes, I don't know how much David told you, but I left in a hurry. I'd only time to pack a few essentials.'

I follow her and she opens a door, saying, 'I hope you'll be comfortable. The room's a bit on the small side.' The old-fashioned rose-covered wallpaper, the white candlewick bedspread on the neatly made single bed give an air of calm to the little room.

I've taken an instant liking to Eve. I'm surprised how different she and David are, in both looks and character. Her quiet ways put me at ease and I say, 'It's lovely; just what I need. I can't thank you enough.'

'It's no problem. I'm glad I can help.'

I put my case onto the bed and ask, 'Do you have a phone? I should ring my daughter. She probably knows I'm in Bristol but I must speak to her.'

'Help yourself. The phone's by the door. While you do that, I'll put the kettle on.'

I try to prepare myself for Kate's temper, but her furious voice demanding, 'Where are you? We've been out of our minds with worry,' shocks me into acknowledging the distress I've caused.

'I'm really sorry,' I say. 'I had to get away. I couldn't stay another moment. Your dad...'

'Alice told me! She said you just upped and left! That Dad's distraught! Where are you? Who are you with?'

'David's sister. She lives in Bristol.'

'David's sister! I didn't know he had a sister. Why didn't you come to me? Why didn't you talk to us? Alice thinks you and David are having an affair. Are you?'

Thankful she can't see the guilt that must be plastered across my face, I raise my voice, saying, 'No! David's a friend. When I arrived in Bristol I rang him. He said his sister had a spare room and he asked her if I could stay there. I'm sorry I didn't talk to you. It was difficult. Sean's your father. You wouldn't understand. Since moving to Ireland things have gone from bad to worse... I couldn't cope.'

A sob catches my voice and she says, 'Mum, please don't cry. What's Eve's address? I want to come and see you.'

'I'd rather you didn't. Not at the moment. I'm tired. I haven't slept properly in ages. Once I get a good night's sleep I'll be more coherent. Can I come to you tomorrow?'

'I'm on a long day. It'll have to be the day after.'

'Okay. I look forward to seeing you Wednesday. What time?'

'Come about four. I'll give Alice and Dad a ring and let them know you're all right. They're both really worried about you. What's Eve's address and telephone number?'

'I'll get them for you right now.'

When I finish speaking to Kate, I go back to the kitchen and Eve asks, 'Was everything alright?'

She hands me a mug of tea and I say, 'Kate's angry. I don't blame her; I left without any warning. I'm seeing her Wednesday. Hopefully, I'll be able to explain things then.'

'Try not to worry. I'm sure when you give your reasons she'll understand. I'm visiting my friend tomorrow so you'll have the flat to yourself. Watch a bit of TV. Use the washing machine if you need to; make yourself at home. Try and relax.'

Her kindness opens a channel and I tell her about my life with Sean. The hopes we had when we bought the house. His alcoholism. The grief I felt when I knew I could no longer live with him.

She takes my hand. 'When you see Kate, tell her what you've told me. She won't fail to understand. I'm going to make us some lunch. After you've eaten, have a lie down. You look exhausted.'

The flannelette sheets, the heavy woollen blankets are unfamiliar. I open my eyes and pink rosebuds swim into view. I remember the wallpaper, that I came for a lie-down after lunch. I hear the clink of bottles, the sound of what could be a milk float. I get out of bed and open the door. The flat is quiet. In the hallway is a note and a key.

Anna, I thought I'd let you sleep. Help yourself to whatever you need. I'll be back about 5.00 p.m. – Eve.

My eyes rest on the phone; resisting the urge to pick it up, I look away and tell myself, you've been a depressing companion; no wonder David wanted to get rid of you. You should take a leaf out of his friend Susie's book. She wouldn't stand by a phone waiting for it to ring, nor would she waste her time crying about things that have gone and passed. You're going to have to shed the clinging person you've become, find a job and be more independent.

Out of nowhere, a shadow falls and Sean comes into my mind. My conscience tells me to write to him, but how can I? The pages will be so full of bitter words. Will reveal such a dark side of my soul. I put the thought aside.

In an effort to clear my head from the past, I get ready and leave the flat. I explore the local High Street and rummage through charity shops. Carrying a bag full of second-hand clothes, I push the door into a greengrocer's. The smell of vegetables, the potatoes, onion and cabbage I put into a basket bring a memory of the garden, a hope that Alice will enjoy taking her food from the ground as much as I did. Next to the counter is a bucket of flowers. I think of Eve and choose a bouquet of yellow globe chrysanthemums for sunshine, blue Michaelmas daisies for a summer sky.

When Eve walks into the kitchen she sniffs the air, looks towards the oven, saying, 'Something smells good.'

'I hope you like cottage pie.'

Her eyes alight on the bouquet of flowers, now in a tall olive-green vase I'd found at the back of a cupboard. Thinking I may have upset her, I say, 'I'm sorry; I didn't mean to...'

She shakes her head and sits at the table. Touches the vase, saying, 'It was my mother's.' She moves the vase towards her, lowers her head to smell the earthy scent of a yellow bloom. She looks towards a sepia photograph where a bride and groom smile from a brown plastic frame. 'My father grew chrysanthemums. Year after year he won the cup. God help me or David if we knocked a head off. Dad used to joke, "a head for a head!" We were happy then. That was until Mum and Dad died in a car crash. David was thirteen.'

'I knew your parents were dead, but I didn't know David was so young when they died.'

Both our parents were only children. If I hadn't offered to look after David he would have been taken into care. I was about to be married. My fiancé didn't want the responsibility of a thirteen-year-old boy so we called the wedding off. I was working as a clerk in a solicitor's office. They were very good, letting me take holiday and unpaid leave when I needed to. The Council let me take over the tenancy of the house. After David graduated from university he decided to share a house with friends. You know how it is: they grow up. They want a life of their own. I managed to get a Council exchange. I've lived here ever since. I retired five years ago. It's a bit lonely sometimes, but I'm quite happy.' She smiles. 'I'm sorry. Listen to me rabbiting on. The food smells delicious. There was no need to go to all that trouble.' She looks at the flowers. 'That vase hasn't seen a bloom since they died. Thank you, Anna. Thank you very much.'

'It was no trouble. The food's almost ready. I did wonder about inviting David.'

'I'm glad you didn't. He's always busy. Never has a moment to himself. When he can, he visits, but I don't like to trouble him. I let him decide when he comes.'

I lay the table, listening as she tells me, 'I always hoped he'd find a nice girl, someone to look after him. I've only been to his apartment once. I did offer to clean it but he wouldn't hear of it. I don't think there's ever been anybody special in his life. I've sort of given up hope.'

'Well, you never know,' I say, putting a plate of cottage pie and vegetables in front of her. 'Life can take some very unexpected turns.'

After we've eaten and cleared the table, Eve leaves the room and comes back with a stack of photograph albums. I see David as a tousled-haired grinning boy. A young man dressed in a cap and gown. I'm drawn into Eve's reminiscence. Her unselfish love for David brings to mind Bridie's love for Christ. Makes me confront a love that would never be enough for me.

Enjoying the sound of crisp leaves underfoot, I take the shortcut through the park. The afternoon sun gives an expectation that everything is well. That Kate will have forgotten her anger, will be ready to listen to me and understand why I had to leave.

I arrive at her door. When the door opens and I look at her face I see something is wrong. She gives me a hard stare and says, 'Come in.' I hesitate. She looks back. 'Well, are you coming?' I close the door behind me and the patch of sun on the doormat disappears. My pulse races as I follow her up the stairs. We enter the flat and she strikes. 'Now we all know,' she says. 'Yes. We all know.' Her voice climbs higher, her words shooting like arrows. 'You can't lie anymore. You left Dad for David!'

I search for ways to defend myself. There are none. I bow my head to escape her steely eyes. 'HOW COULD YOU!' she shouts. 'DAVID, OF ALL PEOPLE. You're disgusting. I couldn't believe it when Alice told me what Craig had told Adam. But it's true. I went to see Vicky. She said she spoke to you and you told her you were leaving Dad for David!'

'I'm sorry. I didn't want to hurt anyone, but... but...'

'No buts, Mum. What you're doing is wrong. Don't you ever bring David here. And as for you? Well... I...'

I look towards the door, wanting to fly from her disapproval. 'I think I'd better go.'

'Yes, I think you should. I don't want you here at the moment.'

In my scramble to leave, I almost fall down the stairs. I fiddle with the lock. I take a breath of cold clean air and run through the park as though the devil is behind me.

Eve looks up from the book she's reading. 'You're back early.' She puts the book down. 'What on earth's the matter?' She stands up and puts her arm around me. 'Come on, sit down.'

I confess everything – my love for David, my deceit, and its discovery. I tell her the plan to let people think our relationship evolved after I left Sean. She listens without question or judgment. When I finish, she says, 'Look Anna, you don't have to pretend anymore. Not now the truth is out. If you want your relationship to work, you and David need to be together. It isn't because I don't want you here, not at all; I just want you both to be happy.' She takes my hand. 'Why don't you call him now.'

He answers straightaway, as though he was expecting my call. 'David! There's no need to hide anymore. They know. Sean, Alice, Kate, they know we're lovers. There's nothing to stop us living together. I've spoken to Eve and she agrees. As soon as I've packed I'm coming to you.'

CHAPTER 16

The garden is almost unrecognisable. My feet are held tight in a sea of mud. There are no birds in the sky, no cattle in the fields, no Blackie waiting for me. I look towards the house. The curtains are drawn. The door is shut. Sean is nowhere to be seen – as the images evaporate I become aware of the body lying next to me. I open my eyes to a dark room, to the shame when I remember.

It was late afternoon when I'd left Eve's. An hour or so later I arrived at David's. I hadn't put my case down before he started telling me how I'd wheedled my way into his life, ruined his friendship with Sean. His words were so hurtful I rose to his anger, screamed that he'd wanted our affair as much as I did. The quarrel grew to such a frenzy, boiled over to such passion, we almost ripped the clothes from each other. The hurt we gave while making love – if you can call it that – was mutual. The scratches on his back, the bruises on my arm, no more than we deserved. When David finished with me, he stood up from the floor and I watched him get dressed. He put on his jacket and I asked if he was going out. Ignoring me, he picked up his car keys, walked out of the room, slamming the door behind him.

After he left, I gathered my clothes from the floor, went to the bedroom, got into bed and listened to what seemed like another world. The ferry made its way to the SS Great Britain. Darkness fell with a flurry of steps and laughter. Sounds faded to silence and I fell into a dream.

I feel as though I am inside a glass bowl, with no incentive to leave. Indifferent to what's happening on the other side of the glass. David brings me drinks that go cold, sandwiches that are left then taken away.

I hear the bedroom door open. David kneels beside me, saying, 'Don't you think it's time you got up? I'm sorry about some of the things I said. We're both to blame.' He touches my shoulder. 'It's not too late. Sean will forgive you. He'll want you to go home.'

A tear wets my lashes, leaves a trail of sadness in its wake.

David takes a deep breath, stands up, saying, 'Well, you can't lie there forever.' He leaves the room. I listen to the apartment door open and close, the welcome silence.

Reluctantly, I sit up. David's right; I can't stay here forever. I rest my back against the headboard, acknowledging the mistake I'd made. I should have known better. David has always been a free spirit. He'll never be any different. Neither will Sean, which is why I can't go home

Getting out of the grubby dressing gown, having a bath encourages me to look through the clothes I'd bought in the charity shops. I put on a red acrylic sweater, a pair of jeans that feel a size too big. I move a pile of papers from David's desk. The little desk clock tells me it's November 7th. I've been here over a week!

A pang of hunger sends me to the kitchen cupboard. A couple of slices of toast and a mug of instant coffee gives me a push towards thinking about contacting the outside world.

My sister won't know I've left Ireland, but I need time to decide how to tell her – Jenny and I haven't been that close since Mum died. Other than Christmas and birthdays, we don't have much contact. Our lives went in different directions after we married. Her wedding to James was a big white affair; their son Stephen was born two years later. Mine was a hurried visit to a registry office; Alice was born five months later. James is sober and steady. To my knowledge, they've never had an upset. Leaving one's husband was not an event that would befall them.

I decide to ring Liz.

The café is packed. I stand on my toes, just managing to see the top of Liz's dark hair and Sue's back-combed, blonde bouffant. I skirt around the tables, making my way towards them, conscious of my ill-fitting clothes. As usual, they've dressed with care.

'Anna, thank God you rang,' says Sue, waving her hand to get the attention of the waitress.

I sit down and Liz says, 'We've been worried about you. Vicky told us over a week ago you were leaving Sean. I rang Ireland and Sean told me you'd left. None of us knew how to get in touch with you.' She looks at Sue for confirmation.

Sue orders me a cappuccino and says, 'Vicky said she'd told Craig, and of course he told Adam.'

'Stupid cow,' says Liz. 'Craig's the last person to confide in.'

Sue nods her head. 'I agree; I don't trust or like him.'

'I don't trust her anymore,' I say.

Sue looks at Liz before turning to me. 'How are you? How's David treating you?'

'Okay. He tries his best. He's upset at the hurt we've caused. And... I don't know... I don't really know what he feels or thinks.'

'He should have thought about who was being hurt before getting you into his bed,' says Liz.

I lower my head and gaze at the flower-patterned tablecloth. Tracing the leaves with my finger, I notice my bitten nails and put them onto my lap, saying, 'We're both to blame; it's as much my fault as his.' I see they are unconvinced.

The waitress brings my coffee and the conversation stalls. We pick up our drinks. Sue puts hers down, hesitates before asking, 'How are the girls? Have you spoken to them since you left?'

'I saw Kate. She's angry. I'm sure Alice feels the same. I wonder if they'll ever speak to me again.'

'When did you see Kate? When was the last time you saw Alice?' persists Sue.

'Alice on the morning I left; Kate just after I arrived here.'

'And Sean?'

I haven't spoken to him since...' The unfinished sentence hangs in the air.

'Do you think you might go back?' asks Liz.

'No. That part of my life is over.'

For a few minutes, nothing more is said. What they believed to be my moment of madness has registered as something far more serious.

Sue's voice breaks the silence. 'You must get in touch with them. If you feel you can't speak, write a letter.'

'It's finding the right words.'

'You will. Take your time. The words will come.'

'Have you thought about buying a mobile phone?' asks Liz. 'I don't suppose they'll ring you at David's. They won't want to talk to that scumbag.'

Sue gives Liz a warning look.

'Well, he is,' says Liz, passing me her phone.

'Are they expensive?' I ask.

'No,' says Sue, rummaging inside her bright pink bag. 'You can get some good deals if you shop round.'

She pulls out a pink phone. 'Look.' She holds it against the bag. 'The perfect match.'

I smile and she asks, 'How are you managing for money?'

'I withdraw money when I need to; the rent from the houses give Sean and I enough to live on. Though I am going to start looking for a job.'

I look at the phones on the table. 'Maybe I'll get myself one. I think it's probably a good idea.'

Sue and Liz bring a little normality into my life. The hour we spend together flies by. Before I know it, Sue is paying the bill and we're saying goodbye, promising to meet in the same place, at the same time next week. I also promise to write a letter to Alice and Kate.

When I get back, I clear a space on the table and take the little grey phone from its box. I give the instruction book a quick scan and put it down. I take the cellophane off the writing pad, pick up a pen and stare at the blank page. Do I tell them I'm happy? Even if that was true, could I say it? Do I say I'm missing them? I miss them terribly. Alice, the children; Kate and her angry words never leave me. Will I see any of them again? What about Sean? I can't bear to think of him. When I do it breaks my heart.

The cleaning begins when I unpack the food I've bought, when I look for a clean place to put them. One thing leads to another. I wash the kitchen cupboards, then the floor, then the bathroom.

Perhaps I wanted to start a fight. All evening I've been sitting in the spotless lounge anticipating David's reaction.

He stands in the doorway. For a moment he's speechless. His face darkens. 'How dare you. If you want to stay here, don't touch or move anything that doesn't belong to you!'

Weary of disappointment, I stand up, saying, 'Don't be so ungrateful; the place was like a pigsty!'

'I like it that way. I don't want some woman coming round with her bloody mop.'

A spark of anger makes me snap. 'Happy as a pig in shit and, while we're about it, one who can't even give his sister the little bit of time and kindness she deserves.'

'Eve is none of your business.'

'You made it my business when you took me there. And it's about time you started repaying some of the sacrifices she made for you.'

'I'm warning you, Anna. I live my life the way I want to. I don't want some fucking woman meddling in it. I didn't invite you to stay here.'

'You're pretty happy to have me around when you want a screw.'

'And don't you like it.' He comes towards me. 'You're gasping for it; you'll open your legs for me any time. You were a bored, sexually frustrated housewife when you came panting at my door.' He pulls me towards him. 'Come on, Anna. You like it as much as I do.'

I am ashamed of myself. When David pulls away from me and says, 'Anna, you're a bloody good fuck,' I make a resolution.

CHAPTER 17

The row certainly made me look at the pathetic creature I've become. Certainly motivates me to stop moping and do something positive with my life. It's a short walk from David's to the job centre. I'm only in there ten minutes. The next thing I know I'm on my way to an interview.

'Can you do Saturdays?' asks the landlord of the Rose and Crown.

'Yes,' I reply.

He gives me a quick talk on health and safety, and I step out of the pub a fully-fledged barmaid.

I'm a few minutes late when I join Sue and Liz at the cafe. 'I've got myself a job. I'm going to be a barmaid,' I say, sitting down to the cup of coffee waiting for me.

'Barmaid!'

'Where?'

'Have you done bar work before?'

'No, but I think I'm going to enjoy it. It's the Rose and Crown. It's not far from David's. Tom – the landlord – is very nice, and the pub's okay. The money's not brilliant but it'll do.'

'It must be a step in the right direction,' says Sue. 'You look a lot better than you did last week.'

'Being with you two made me realise I had to stop moping and get a life.'

'You're full of surprises,' says Liz. 'You certainly move fast when you want to. Did you write to the girls?'

'I tried a few times and gave up. But I will, I promise. Though I do wonder if I'll ever be ready to contact Sean.'

Dear Alice,

I stop writing and try again.

I don't know how to begin to tell you how sorry I am for the distress I have caused. I lied to you. The only thing I can say in my defence is that I thought I was doing it for the right reasons. I didn't want to hurt Sean any more than I could avoid.

I rest my hand on the table and read what I've just written. The words are lying. I'd wanted to tell the truth from the very beginning. David was the one who wanted to keep our affair a secret, and I'd gone along with it, blindly believing that it was for the best. That everything was going to have a happy ending. Should I mention David? What is there to say? We pass like ships in the night. The only thing we have in common is sex.

I put the pen back to the paper.

I miss you all so very much, I worry about the damage I have done to our relationship. I fully understand both yours and Kate's anger. It's asking a lot, but I would love to hear from you. I know you won't want to ring me at David's, but a letter? I have bought a mobile phone – the number is at the top of the page.

Tell Sean I will write to him, but...

I rest the pen on the paper, wondering when I'm ever going to be able to find the right words, the different emotions and feelings I have for him, if I will ever be able to rid myself of this consuming anger. I pick up the pen.

...at the moment my mind is in too much of a turmoil to understand myself, let alone explain my actions to Sean. Tell him I am feeling better, and that I am starting work next Saturday. It's a bar job. The pay's not too bad so he won't have to worry about me dipping into our bank account.

I'm sure your father needs a lot of support. It wasn't what you expected when you moved to Ireland. I can only hope you will forgive me some time in the future.

Give my love to the children.

Lots of love, Mum.

I write a similar letter to Kate.

Tom's voice comes from the far end of the bar, 'Thanks, Anna. See you tomorrow.' I leave the pub, turning up my coat collar as I go out into the cold night air. There is no one around, the only sound my footsteps on the pavement. I think about the elderly gentleman who'd ordered a whiskey on the rocks. He'd told me I had nice eyes. I glanced at myself in the pub mirror and saw a middle-aged woman with a sad face. I touch the wage packet in my pocket, wondering if I should I spend some of it on a haircut? I'm still mulling over how to make my money last the week when I arrive at David's.

I walk into the lounge. David looks up from reading his paper, saying, 'You'll never guess who rang this evening?'

'No. Who?'

'Diane. She's just come back from Ireland.'

I take off my coat, remembering that she had said she was planning to visit us in November. I hesitate before asking, 'Did she say how Sean was?'

'She didn't say much about her visit, or Sean. She just gave me an ear bashing. She wouldn't let me get a word in edgeways. In fact, I put the phone down on her.'

I make myself a drink. David and I never mention Sean. We stay clear of subjects such as Ireland, my daughters, his sister. That way we seem to rub shoulders in a distant but reasonable way.

I look up at Eve's window, giving her one last wave. Wanting a quick change of clothes before going to work, I walk briskly. A phone rings – suddenly I realise it's mine. I rummage through my bag, look at the phone, trying to remember which button to press, nearly dropping it when I hear Kate's voice.

'Yes, yes... Anywhere... I don't mind where we meet,' I say.

It's such a relief to see her. She smiles, an uncertain smile, but a smile all the same. She walks towards where I'm sitting. I stand up, not knowing whether to take her in my arms or not. Her chin quivers – a characteristic inherited from my mother. 'Mum, I'm so, so sorry.'

Ignoring the interested stares, we hold each other. 'Don't cry,' I say. 'It's all right. Everything's going to be all right.'

'I shouldn't have shouted at you. I shouldn't have... I'm so very sorry.'

'Well, that makes two of us. Two sorries add up to a huge amount of forgiveness. Sit down. Let me buy you a drink.'

Seeing her lifts me into a brighter world, makes me aware of the clatter of cups, the animated faces of staff and customers, the music coming through a speaker.

I return with the drinks. 'How are you?' she asks.

'All the better for seeing you; I'm so glad you came.'

The smile hasn't left my face. I don't want this feeling of joy to leave me but there are questions I must ask. 'How's Alice? How... how's your dad?'

'Not good; Alice is very angry with you. And Dad... well, we're all worried about him. Adam's very supportive; he sees Dad most days, and it was a godsend that Diane went over. Did you know she'd arranged a visit?'

'Yes, I'd heard she'd gone over.'

'She was a great help. Dad hadn't been looking after himself, not eating properly, drinking heavily. That's why

Alice is so upset. She feels you left her in the lurch. Anyway, Diane took complete control of the situation. She cleaned the house from top to bottom, cooked him decent meals. Alice said Diane had even prevented him driving into town for more booze. By all accounts, she threatened to go home if he did!'

I take a deep breath, thinking, if only it could have been that easy.

'They must have got on well,' continues Kate, 'because she's going over to spend Christmas with him.'

Christmas. For years I've hated them, so why this feeling of unease? Why is there a sting in my voice when I say, 'That'll be a challenge for her.'

The conversation stalls. We pick up our cups. She puts hers down, saying, 'The other thing is I've decided to spend Christmas in Ireland.'

I feel a rush of disappointment as she explains. 'The managers at work have been very understanding. Sam's offered to cover my shifts. He's such an angel. I don't know what I would have done without him.' She looks at me with concern. 'What are you doing for Christmas?'

I don't want her to feel responsible for what I do, and I say, 'I'm not sure. I've hardly thought about it. I spoke to your Auntie Jenny. I told her what's happened, and she's invited me to stay some time over Christmas.'

'Aren't you spending it with David?'

I fiddle with the handle of my cup. I've avoided mentioning his name. I take a tissue from my pocket and wipe my nose. 'Excuse me, I think I might have a cold coming.' I put the tissue back into my pocket. She looks at me, waiting.

'Oh. Yes, Christmas; I wrote and told you about my job – well, I might have to work. I thought about inviting David's sister to join us, but she's going to a friend's. By all accounts she always spends Christmas with her. And then there's

Susie; she's a friend of David's. She's invited him, I mean us, to her place for Christmas dinner. She has that big gallery at the top of Park Street. By all accounts she puts on quite a grand affair. Lots of interesting people, so I'm told, will be there. If I go, I'll stand out like a sore thumb.' I give Kate a quick smile. 'Anyway, whether I go to Jenny's, or Susie's, or spend the day at work, I won't be cooking. And that's a bonus, isn't it?'

CHAPTER 18

I put the parcel onto the post office scales. I'd been meticulous when I wrapped it, made sure each fold in the paper was perfect and that the string was tightly tied. 'That'll be £5.30,' says the girl behind the counter. I watch her put four colourful red and gold stamps depicting the 'Three Kings' and an airmail sticker onto the brown paper then I push the correct money through the hatch.

The parcel contains a toy each for the children, a necklace made of rose quartz – her birthstone – for Alice and three pairs of socks for Adam. I'd been indecisive about sending a gift to Sean. After much deliberation I put a card in the parcel wishing him a merry Christmas and saying I'd be in touch in the New Year.

I make my way to the exit, wondering if sending the card was the right thing to do. Whether I should I have written more or less or just signed my name. As I wait at the door for a stream of people carrying cards and parcels to pass through, I think about Alice. It's been three weeks since I posted her letter and I haven't heard a word. In less than two weeks, Kate will be in Ireland. When she comes back, what news will she bring?

The doorway clears and I leave the building. An east wind has sent a flurry of snow. I listen to the children's excitement and yearn for my grandchildren. The silver reindeers and the man dressed as Father Christmas magnifies my grief, makes me want to fall into a deep sleep and not wake up until this banishment from their lives has been lifted.

I was disappointed when Tom told me the pub will be closed on Christmas Day. He was certainly happy when I volunteered to work Christmas Eve and Boxing Day, which means I shall visit Jenny sometime before New Year.

David was noncommittal when I told him I wanted some time on my own and wouldn't be going to Susie's. So you can imagine my disappointment when she rang and insisted I join her and her friends for lunch. Unable to think of a good excuse, I accepted.

I open my eyes. The first thing I notice is that David's side of the bed has not been slept in. I peep out from the warmth of the duvet. The curtains are wide open and a grey light fills the room. After the pub closed, Tom invited me to stay behind for a Christmas drink; the one too many cocktails have left me with a slight hangover.

I look at the clock. It's 11:16. The children will have opened their presents. Three months have gone since I last saw them. Stella will probably be crawling. They grow so fast I'll hardly recognise them. Stella won't remember me but Ella will. What has she been told, does she hear whispers, or am I not spoken about?

Will Sean's Christmas end the way it always has – lying on the floor in a drunken stupor? Or did he wake with clear eyes? Is Diane at his side?

It's now 11:36. Reluctantly, I push the duvet aside.

'Darling, we thought you were never coming.' Susie's hair and clothes ooze expense, her tight-fitting black dress beautifully adorned with a red chunky necklace and matching earrings, her hair cut in a way that will need constant visits to the hairdresser, her make-up so impeccably applied that even when she comes close to kiss my cheek, there's not a sign of clogged mascara.

'I'm sorry,' I say. 'I over-slept.' I take off my coat, conscious that my brown lace-up shoes and corduroy trousers – worn for the comfort of walking – will be seen as frumpish.

She takes my coat, gives it a little shake, exclaiming, 'It's wet. Aren't you hot in that jumper?'

'It's cold outside. It's started snowing again.'

'You poor thing; I'd forgotten you don't drive. Never mind, I'll put this in the utility room, then I'll take you to meet the others.'

She disappears into the kitchen and I look into the hall mirror. She's left a lipstick print on my cheek. I rub at it, spreading the lipstick – that is now on my finger – onto the other cheek. She comes back into the hall, looks at me and says, 'That's better; a little blusher does wonders,' and takes my arm.

'I've brought wine,' I say, slipping my arm from hers and taking the bottle from my bag. 'It's white. I thought we'd probably be having turkey and...'

She takes the bottle from me and looks at the label. 'Australian.'

'Yes, Chardonnay. Tom, the landlord of the pub I work in says it's very nice.'

'I'm sure it is. I'll put it in the fridge for later.' She leaves the bottle on the hall table and ushers me into the dining room. I quickly count seven people sat around a beautifully laid table, sparkling with Christmas decorations and lighted candles. David is speaking in earnest to an attractive woman with sleek, platinum blonde hair. Whatever he's saying is amusing. She's still laughing when Susie calls, 'At last, Anna has arrived.'

David looks up. I can see from his expression he'd rather I wasn't here.

'Let me introduce you to everyone,' says Susie. She touches the springy black curls of a man with his back to us, saying, 'This is Michael.' The man turns towards me, revealing a handsome profile then a sensual smile. 'Michael

~ 148 ~

painted those delightful murals in the Council building. He can be a bit of a pain, but you must excuse him. He has the mind of an eight-year-old, which is why he likes painting on walls.'

Michael gives me a mischievous wink.

'Next to him is Carrie.' – I look at an elegant woman wearing a gold-sequined top. 'The jewellery she designs is fabulous. Charles actually bought a piece for Camilla.'

Carrie's long painted-red fingernails give a little wave.

'The gorgeous man next to her is Jasper. He's the architect who designed the new theatre in Redland. Have you been there?'

I shake my head as Jasper gives a half smile and a nod.

'Christina.' Susie points towards the woman who's been talking with David. 'She's made her money from being beautiful.'

'And a lot of hard work; modelling can be exhausting,' says Christina.

'The bedsores must have been painful,' shouts Michael.

Christina picks up a cracker and throws it at him.

Susie claps her hands. 'Children, children, stop it. What must Anna think of us?' She looks at David then at me, saying, 'Of course, there's no need to introduce you two.' She points to a young girl with red spiky hair. 'Jeanie is an art student. I tell you, darling, her work is going to revolutionise the art world.'

Jeanie gives me a big bright smile.

'Finally, but not least, is Roger.' Susie rests her hand on the shoulder of the person on our right. 'He's a pyrotechnic sculptor. He makes huge wooden sculptures then sets fire to them. They're absolutely amazing.' Roger's tangled grey head gives no indication he's heard what's been said, let alone felt the hand on his shoulder.

Susie puts her arm around me, saying, 'Anna is a barmaid. I'm sure she has plenty of stories to tell about the people who frequent her pub.' She pulls out the chair between Michael and Roger, inviting me to sit down. 'Let me pour you a drink.' She takes a bottle from the ice bucket. 'I presume you like Chablis.'

Toying with the stem of my glass, I look around the table. Everyone is in some sort of conversation with someone. Feeling out of my depth, I look at the square workman-like hands of the silent pyrotechnic, unsure how to begin a conversation with him.

A few minutes go by and Susie wheels in a trolley loaded with food. 'Thank heaven for Waitrose,' she says, putting smoked salmon, pâté, prawns and an assortment of salads onto the table. 'The pâté's veggie and untainted. Unlike the poor chestnut loaf that's sharing the oven with a murdered pig. I must explain to the vegetarians that, for carnivores, Christmas won't be Christmas, without a piece of flesh.'

'Let's raise a toast to the chestnut loaf,' shouts Michael, standing unsteadily to his feet, 'and also to flesh, dead or alive.' He grins, falls back into his chair with a thump.

Other than the occasional splutter of laughter from Carrie whenever Michael whispers in her ear, conversation is reduced to a few words between mouthfuls. Roger, completely engrossed in his food, clearly feels no obligation to talk. And, I must say, neither do I.

When everyone has finished eating, Jeanie collects the plates and takes them into the kitchen. I'm watching David reading the fortune fish that lies in Christina's palm, when suddenly Michael's voice asks, 'How do you know Susie?'

'Through David,' I say.

'Are you another of David's ex's?'

'No. We live together.'

Michael refills his glass, holds it up for all to see, saying, 'I would like to raise another toast, this time to Anna. Somehow she's managed to tame David; they're living together.' He leans towards me. I feel the heat on my cheeks as he says, 'I hear he has an insatiable sexual appetite! Hey David,' he calls, 'I'm surprised you haven't worn her out.'

'I'm working on it,' shouts David, above Jasper's burst of laughter, 'but if I need to, I'll give you a call.'

'What's the commotion?' exclaims Susie, coming into the room with a trolley now loaded with sliced pork and a chestnut loaf.

'It's David,' says Michael. 'He's met his match with Anna. I thought he might need a hand. We haven't shared a woman since... when was it, Susie?'

'How would I know? I'm sure it would be unmemorable!'

Feeling at a loss, I grip the edge of the table. A large work-hardened hand covers mine and I look up into Roger's warm brown eyes. His smile crinkles the weather beaten skin, reminds me that winter walks and the smell of bonfires are out there, waiting to be enjoyed.

'Children, children,' calls Susie, tapping a teaspoon against her glass. 'You're embarrassing poor Anna. She's new to your decadent ways. Give her time. I'm sure it won't be long before your wickedness rubs off on her.'

'Ah, women,' mumbles Michael. 'When they reach fifty they've had it.' He turns his attention to Jeanie. 'What about you? Would you warm an old man's bed?'

Jeanie, eager to please, smiles uncertainly. I feel her embarrassment. Still holding Roger's hand, I stand up and cast my eye around the table. I see them, stark and uncovered, the make-up and smart clothes, the designer aftershave and expensive haircuts, as transparent as the glass baubles decorating the table.

Their laughter fades and I say, 'That's better; Susie's gone to all this trouble and you're behaving like a load of kids. I would like to propose a toast, this time to Susie.' They lift their glasses. I sit down, mindful that the atmosphere has changed.

Susie pats my shoulder, 'Thank you, darling. It's nice to be appreciated.' Jeanie gives me a radiant smile as she follows Susie into the kitchen. Carrie gives Michael a quiet telling off. Christina turns from David to talk to Jasper.

Roger takes my hand and says, 'Well done, my dear.'

I look at the frayed edges of his sleeves, admiring his obvious lack of concern regarding what the rest of the company thinks or wears. 'Why are you here?' I ask. 'How do you know these people?'

'I'm here for the food, my dear. My love of carnal delights has diminished. But good food, well, that's another matter, and Susie is a bloody good cook.' He helps himself to a large spoonful of roast potatoes, tips them onto the mound of sliced pork that Jeanie had put on his plate. 'As for how I know them, well, I don't. Garden clearance is my occupation, bonfires my hobby. They go hand in hand. A few years ago I began making large pieces of artwork from scrap wood. Nobody thought them as interesting as I did. They began to clutter the piece of land around my caravan, so I started to burn them. Since then, well, I have my choice of invites.' He picks up a serving spoon, takes a heap of Brussels sprouts, saying, 'And I always accept those where I know the food will be good.'

Roger retreats into the delight of gluttony. And I? A certain sense of pride has lifted my chin. I no longer worry about who David is talking to or what he might be saying. A little glimmer of light in the dark shadow of my mind tells me I might begin to like myself.

Crackers have been pulled, jokes shared. Susie invites everyone to sit around the open fire in the lounge.

I offer to help clear the table and wash up. 'The dishwasher will do that,' says Susie with a smile, 'but I'd be grateful for a hand with the clearing. We'll let Jeanie join the others. She'll breathe some youth into their addled brains.'

We go into the dining room. Susie blows out the candles and turns on the overhead light. We clear the table and, piece by piece, bit by bit, the memory of a lonely embarrassed woman is scraped into the bin. Only the flashing tree, dimmed by the glare of the electric light, suggests there may have been a party.

We are in the kitchen when Susie says, 'Anna...'

I pass a pile of rinsed plates to her. 'Yes?'

She bends over to load them into the dishwasher.

'Yes?' I repeat.

She stands up and turns to face me. 'I hope you don't mind. I don't want to intrude. It's your business, of course.'

'Go on.'

She turns her back to me, picks up a cloth and wipes at the spotless draining board.

'What do you want to say?'

She faces me and rests herself against the sink, saying, 'David and I have known each other a long time.' She hesitates. 'We've had many... when I say many, I mean our relationship has taken different forms. It's just that, I don't want you to get hurt. I know what he's like. He's never going to...'

She gives me a sad smile, shrugs her shoulders and the Susie who invited me to dinner reappears. 'Him and I are two of a kind.' She laughs. 'It's a big world; only a fool would want to eat the same meal every day.'

The cutlery rattles as she pushes and slides the dishes into the machine. A jab at the switch and the water begins to pour.

'Come on,' she says. 'Let's join the others.'

Through the utility doorway I see my coat draped over a stool. Susie stops by the kitchen door and looks at me. 'Are you coming?'

I go towards my coat and pick it up. 'I feel it's time for me to leave.'

'But it's early,' she says, glancing at the clock.

I slip my arms into the coat sleeves. 'You were right,' I say, fastening the buttons. 'It's a big world. I need to discover who I am and where I want to be...'

'I'm sorry if I've upset you.'

'No, you haven't. In fact, I feel liberated.'

'How will you get back?'

'I'll walk.' I pull the curtain aside. 'It's stopped snowing; look how lovely it is.'

Together we look onto a different world. A carpet of snow, as white and clean as when it fell from the sky, shimmers under the street lighting; a world as alien and silent as the moon.

'Are you sure you'll be all right walking back?'

'Yes, I'll enjoy it.'

We move away from the window. 'Can David stay here tonight?' I ask. 'It's just that he's been drinking – the roads may be icy and...'

'Yes, I understand,' she says.

We go into the hallway. 'I must say goodbye.'

Faces turn as I open the lounge door. 'Are you going?' asks Jeanie from her seat on the floor, her face flushed from the fire.

'Yes, I'm working tomorrow. The following day I'm going to visit my sister in Southampton.'

Michael is asleep, his head lolled on the back of the sofa, his mouth wide open. Jasper, so very obviously drunk, spills amber liquid from the whiskey glass held perilously in his hand. Carrie gives a bored kind of smile. Christina looks up from the glossy magazine she's reading.'

I look at David. 'Susie said you're welcome to stay here tonight.'

He gives a sheepish smile.

Roger gives the chocolate he's eating one last smack of his lips before saying, 'Goodnight, Anna. We may not meet again, but remember: shelter, food and warmth are all we need; anything else is just weight we have to carry.'

I look at his ample frame. He pops another chocolate into his mouth, and I say, 'Goodnight all.'

The Chardonnay still stands on the hall table. 'Take care,' says Susie, kissing my cheek.

The cold clear air clears my nose, fills my lungs, sharpens my thoughts, sets them free. From here I can go wherever I choose.

The train gathers speed as it leaves Southampton station. Jenny's anxious face when we said goodbye on the platform brought memories of our childhood. After Dad died, Mum worked all the hours God sent. Jenny and I comforted each other, shared a bed, our sweets, our fears. She wore my clothes when I outgrew them. Our lives went in different directions, but there are moments when the past rushes forward and we are children again. I smile to myself. Jenny's concern for me was touching. I tried to assure her that – yes, I was all right. Of course I was upset about Alice and worried about Sean. I told her I was planning to go to Ireland after the New Year. Her questions about David were more difficult to answer – he still hadn't come home when I left to catch my train the morning after Boxing Day. I made light of our affair, saying I thought David was the catalyst, but leaving Sean was the right thing to do. I told her I didn't know if David and I will stay together. When she asked if I loved him, I said I'd confused love with romance and passion but I know the difference now.

I juggle my overnight bag with the key to David's apartment and open the door. The bathroom tap is running; I call hello and take my bag into the bedroom. On the rug next to the unmade bed is a cold cup of tea. I bend over to pick it up. The silver foil catches my eye straight away.

It doesn't surprise or upset me. I'd made my mind up already. I push open the bathroom door. David opens a sleepy eye and sinks further into the deep bath. 'Come and feel,' he murmurs, slipping his hand under the water.

I was going to show him the empty Durex pack, ask who she was, but instead I squeeze the foil, put it into the bathroom bin and say, 'I'm not stopping; it's time I left.'

Before he can answer, I go into the hall, pick up the phone and dial Liz's number. 'Liz, I know it's presumptuous, but can I come and sleep on your sofa? It won't be for long, about a month, if that's okay?'

CHAPTER 19

It was staying with Jenny and James that made me look at my life. The breath of normality they gave showed just how abusive my relationship with David had become. Finding the empty Durex packet was just what I needed to deliver a final push.

David must have been listening to me talking to Liz. Within seconds of me putting the phone down, I heard him getting out of the bath. Within minutes he was standing at the bedroom doorway with a towel wrapped around his waist, asking if I needed any help. I'd acquired a few more clothes since leaving Ireland and asked if he had a couple of carrier-bags. He went out of the room, came back with two Tesco bags and left me to finish packing. When the room was clear of my things, I picked up my little brown suitcase and the two full carrier bags. 'Your key's on the bedside table,' I told him. He waited at the door for me to leave then shut it behind me. We didn't even say goodbye.

When I walked out of the building, a flock of pigeons flew from the pavement. I watched them soar. Felt their freedom in my step. A taxi appeared and, throwing thrift to the wind, I hailed it.

'Anna! Come in. I'm so glad to see you.'

I step into Liz's flat, drop my case and bags onto the floor and hug her. 'I'm glad to be here. It won't be for long – I promise.'

'Shh. You can stay as long as you like. Let me take your coat.' She helps me off with my coat, puts it on a hanger and ushers me into the sitting room. 'I'm glad I was here to take your call. I nearly stayed a few extra days at Mum's. Sit down. Make yourself at home while I put the kettle on.'

Despite the view from the window being one of sleet and a darkening sky, the mere fact that I'm sitting on Liz's futon and my belongings are inside her house brings a kindle of light into my life. Liz passes me my drink, sits next to me, saying, 'I hope you'll find the futon comfortable.'

'Just being here's a comfort. It won't be for long. I'm going to give the tenant in Wellington Road a month's notice. When she leaves, I'll move in.'

'There's no rush.'

I give her a fond smile. 'Thanks, Liz. A stay with you is just what I need, but I can't wait to settle down in a home of my own.'

'I quite understand. You won't know yourself. I've lived on my own for nearly ten years and can honestly say I haven't regretted one minute of it.' Putting on a more serious face, she asks, 'What happened between you and David?'

I look across the room as though the answer might be there.

'I understand if you don't want to talk, but...'.

'There's not much to say. David and I... it wasn't what we... it wasn't what I hoped for.'

'Well, if you need to... when you're ready...' She looks at my case and the carrier-bags. 'You haven't got much. You'll probably get it into my wardrobe. When you've finished your tea, go and unpack. I'll give Sue a ring and invite her round to dinner.'

I've been told to make myself comfortable and I sit in the one comfortable chair, listening to their chatter. Liz snaps, 'Fuck. The sausages are burnt.'

Sue says, 'Not to worry. Where's the corkscrew?' I close my eyes, enjoying the minor details that make life so satisfyingly ordinary.

The burnt sausages, jacket potatoes and Asda's special offer wine are as good as any festive feast. We finish eating. Liz asks, 'Do you fancy something sweet? I've a tin of rice in the cupboard.'

'Just a little,' whispers Sue, unable to hide her pleasure. 'I'm trying to lose weight. The boys are no help. They're always buying me chocolates. I do wish they wouldn't.' She looks at me with a frown. 'It's all right for you. You need fattening up. Though there's not much chance of that happening here. Not with Liz's cooking. She pats her ample stomach. 'Perhaps I'd better move in.'

Liz comes into the room, carrying a tray holding three dishes. 'Bloody cheek,' she says, putting a dish in front of Sue. 'Cordon Bleu would be wasted on you, and the proof will be in the way you wolf that down.'

'What a way to treat guests,' laughs Sue, looking at me. 'How long do you think you'll put up with her?'

'As long as she'll have me. I'm giving the tenant in Wellington Road a month's notice. When she leaves I'll move in. The other thing is I want to go to Ireland. I need to try and heal some of the hurt I've caused and I want to see the children. Kate flew back today. She'll be home by now. We're going to meet up for coffee. I'm desperate to know what's happening.'

She hasn't unbuttoned her coat and I'm firing Kate with questions. 'How are they? Did the children like their presents? How was Sean?'

'Where would you like me to begin?' she says as she sits down. 'The children are fine. Stella's crawling and into everything. I'm sure she'll be walking soon. Ella loved the game you sent. Of course, there were a few tears. What with Stella trying to get her hands on Ella's toys and not wanting to go to bed.'

'And Alice...?'

'She's still angry. And I can understand why. I'd probably feel the same if I were her.'

For a moment neither of us speak, then I say, 'What about Sean?'

'Better for Diane being there. Alice said he cheered up considerably after she arrived. He gets lonely. He misses you, Mum.'

A rush of guilt takes the words from my mouth, leaves them floating in the space between us.

'What about your Christmas, Mum? Did you enjoy it? What did you do?'

'I... Me and David... went to Susie's.' I hunt for an explanation. 'That's when David and I felt things weren't going as well as we'd hoped. I wanted to think things over and spent a few days with Jenny. When I got back, David and I agreed the best thing was for me to move out. At the moment, I'm staying with Liz.'

She looks at me in astonishment. 'You certainly move fast.'

'I'm giving Emma, the tenant in Wellington Road, notice to leave. When she's gone, I'll move in.'

'So leaving Dad, the upheaval, the upset it caused, was all for nothing.'

'No. It's not like that. I wasn't happy. Sean and I... I had to go.'

Tears fill her eyes.

'I'm sorry. I don't want you to think I might go back. The mistake was leaving the way I did. After I've moved into Wellington Road, I'm going to Ireland. I'm going to try and make Alice and Sean understand the reasons I left.'

We finish our coffee in silence. We go outside and stand in the café doorway, sheltering from the rain. 'It came as a shock,' she says. 'I don't know you anymore. What you'll be doing next.'

'Once I'm settled, when I have a home of my own, I'll be happy.'

'I hope so.' She gives me a peck on the cheek. 'If you need a hand moving let me know.'

Emma's sob becomes a wail. 'But where am I supposed to go? What about my cats?'

'I'm sure you'll find a...'

'And the decorating; I've spent a fortune.'

'I'm sorry. I'll give you a good reference.'

'If I'd known you were coming back so soon, I wouldn't have...'

'I know. I'm sorry. We'll say a month from today. The 3rd of February. Is that okay?'

She slams the receiver down. I realise I've gone about this in the wrong way. I shouldn't have told her over the phone. Sometimes I don't know the right way from the wrong way. The right words from the wrong words. I put the phone into its cradle and pick up the pen. I look at the blank piece of paper on the table in front of me, asking myself, where are the words I need now?

Dear Sean

This is the hardest letter I've ever had to write. I've behaved abominably, but I can't change what happened. I shouldn't have gone with David. It was wrong. Try to forgive him; he tried to dissuade me from leaving you. He valued your friendship, but I selfishly and foolishly pushed myself on him. I made him an offer he found hard to refuse. It's taken a little while for me to come to my senses, but I see now that I used him. I know you don't want to hear these words but our marriage was not a happy one. I'm not sorry I left you. I am sorry I destroyed your friendship.

David and I are no longer together. At the moment I'm staying with Liz. I need a place to live so I've given Emma notice to leave the house. I hope to move in some time in February. This will mean you'll receive less rent.

We need to talk. After I move, I would like to come to Miltown and speak with you. I hope I'll be able to stay with Alice. I wrote to her a while back but she hasn't replied, and I'm not sure I'm welcome. Whatever, I will definitely come, even if I stay in a B & B.

Yours, Anna

I re-read the letter. Pore over the sentences. Consider each word until, almost satisfied, I put it into the envelope.

I'm excited about moving into the house, but there was also a tinge of sadness when I said goodbye to Liz and she left for work. I look at the overflowing boxes, the bulging black plastic sacks piled on the floor – Liz and Sue had searched their cupboards, begged from family and friends and now the mismatched bedding, the paraphernalia that make a home is ready to be transferred into Kate's car.

It's a short drive to Wellington Road. We park and, for a brief moment, I stay in the car, gazing at the house, wondering if it will give me the happiness I'm looking for.

Kate opens the passenger door, asking, 'Are you coming?' I take the key from my purse and step out onto the pavement.

The essence of the girl who lived here still lingers – the mark on the wall where a picture had hung. The dead pot plant next to the phone, the smell of cat's pee.

'The place stinks. Did you know she had cats?' asks Kate.

'She had a cat.'

'More like half a dozen. Come on, let's get these bags in,' and in less than fifteen minutes my possessions are piled onto the floor in the tiny sitting-room.

'Those walls are a revolting colour and that sofa is disgusting!' says Kate.

I put on a brave face. 'It'll be fine after a few coats of paint and I can put a throw over the sofa.'

'It might need more than a few coats. God knows what the rest of the house is like.'

The rest of the house is much the same. The furniture that Sean and I had left is shabby but serviceable. 'Give it a few weeks and I'll be inviting you and Sam to supper.'

'It seems a mammoth task to me.'

A knock on the door interrupts us. I recognise Blodwyn straight away – how could I forget the cheery smile, the platinum hair, the colourful, skimpy outfit. 'I wondered if you'd like a cuppa,' she says.

I turn to Kate. 'A cup of tea would be nice.'

'Thanks, Blodwyn. That would be lovely. I'm moving back into the house. This is my daughter, Kate.'

'Emma told me you were coming back. She was very upset. A nice girl, but I won't be sorry to see the back of those bloody cats. They were forever digging up the garden. Is Sean with you?'

'No. I'm on my own.' She's waiting to be told more. 'We must get on,' I say.

'Of course, I'll put the kettle on.'

Kate picks up the empty mugs, saying, 'I'll give these back on my way out. Are you sure you'll be alright?'

'Yes, I'm fine. Don't worry about me.'

'Okay. See you Saturday. Sam's cooking, so don't be late.'

I wait until she drives away. For the first time in my life, I'm on my own, in charge of my own destiny. I go from room to room, looking at every detail, making plans. The small back room with the view of the garden will be my bedroom. Suddenly I want to dance. Humming a tune, holding out my arms, I go into the larger front bedroom and I spin like a top.

I'd only been here a couple of days when the letter from Alice arrived. Since then I've read it so many times I know it by heart. Still, the compulsion to look at her handwriting, to read the words, overrides anything I might be doing.

Dear Mum

Dad told me that you'd written to him and you're planning to come to Miltown. He was very upset that you hadn't said you were coming home, but he showed me your letter and asked me if I would mind if you stayed with me. I told him if it was all right with him then you are welcome.

You may wonder why I didn't reply to your last letter, but the truth is I've felt very hurt and angry. Supporting Dad through these past months has been very draining and I only hope that seeing you won't put him back to where he was three months ago.

We are all relieved to know that you're no longer with David. The anguish Dad felt knowing his wife and best friend had deceived him and were living together had been torment.

I've told Ella you may be coming and she is very excited. Let me know when to expect you.

Alice.

There's no "with love". No kisses. But the letter brings hope. I tuck it back into its envelope and put it safely behind the clock. I'm about to pick up the paintbrush and the tin of paint, when a knock on the door makes me heave a sigh of annoyance. Telling myself I'm going to have to tell Blodwyn that with only one day a week off work I haven't time for endless chatter, I go to answer it.

Vicky gives me a nervous smile. I haven't spoken to her since that night in Miltown. The night I told her I was leaving Sean.

'Can I come in?'

I stand aside and she steps into the hallway, follows me into the kitchen.

'I want to tell you how sorry I am. Sue suggested I came to see you. I don't want to go on like this, not talking, not seeing one another. I'm sorry. I shouldn't have said anything to Craig.'

Vicky has been on my mind. I've acknowledged the fact that I wanted to be angry with someone. It made it easy for that someone to be her. 'You telling Craig made no difference. People would have found out soon enough. Sit down. I'm the one who should be sorry. I've been such a fool. I'm very glad you're here.'

The painting is forgotten; there are too many things waiting to be said. I tell her of my planned trip to Ireland, my worries and concerns. I tell her about my job, that I enjoy it but the journey across town is expensive and time-consuming. When she picks up her coat to leave she says, 'Would you like your old job back? The man who took over from you leaves at the end of the month. I could make it known that you're interested in coming back.'

My bus is at the far end of the road. I wait for a space in the traffic then run to the bus-stop. My phone rings and I take it from my bag, hoping it's not Eve – I find her constant worrying over David difficult to listen to. I put the phone to my ear.

'Is that Anna? It's Margaret, Margaret Davies. Vicky said you might be interested in coming back to work for us.'

CHAPTER 20

When I lived near this town, did I notice the many shades of grey, the buildings, the slate roofs, the paving, the road, the church pointing its steeple towards a grey sky?

I take the short-cut through the church grounds. When I reach the road, I look into the distance, past Alice's bungalow, on and on until the sky and the sea become one. I wonder if I ever really left this place, why it draws me to it.

Feeling apprehensive, I stand at Alice's gate. Her door opens. 'You're late,' she says. 'I thought you weren't coming.'

I step onto the garden path. She disappears into the house and I follow her retreating back, calling, 'The coach was held up; it was an hour late getting into Ennis. I missed the bus and had to hitch. I couldn't ring; I forgot my phone.'

I go into the kitchen, unsure whether to sit or stand.

'Do you want tea?' Without waiting for an answer, she grabs the kettle, fills the room with the bang of cupboard doors and the clash of cutlery.

I put my case and bag down and sit at the table. She puts my tea in front of me; stands with her back to a unit, taking hurried sips from her mug.

'Where are the children?' I ask.

'Adam's taken them to the beach. He wanted to give us time together. He'll be back soon.'

'I'm sorry I'm late.' I give a nervous laugh. 'I haven't hitched since my teens. I...'

'Why have you come here, Mum?'

'I want to see you. I need to explain about David. I can see now, how I used him. He was a means of escape. I was desperate to get away. It was wrong of me.'

'Yes, you were! You behaved like a stupid, love-struck teenager. You didn't care who you hurt, as long as...'

'I'd better go,' I say, picking up my bag.

She holds up her hand. 'Don't. Ella's been looking to forward to you coming. They'll be back soon.'

Still clutching my bag, I sit down. She moves to the table, sits opposite me, saying, 'Those past months were dreadful. Dad's drinking spiralled out of control and I had to deal with it, in a strange country, with two young children.'

'You had Adam.'

'Adam was worried sick about money. We thought he and Dad would work together, but Dad was too ill, was drinking so heavily he couldn't face the day.'

'I'm sorry.' – How many times must I say that word. Sorry for the hurt, sorry for the rift I've caused. Sorry, sorry, but sorry is not enough – 'I'll do all I can, anything to make amends.'

'The only thing you can do is come back, but you won't do that, will you?'

I shake my head and silence falls like a blanket of thistles, scratched with my thoughtless words and wrong-doings.

A door opens and a breath of fresh air brings the laughter of a child, touches the room like a magic wand. Ella runs into the kitchen, stops when she sees me. 'Hello,' I say.

She looks at me shyly, then turns back into the passage; when she returns she's clutching tightly to Adam's hand. 'Aren't you going to say hello to Nana?' he says.

She shakes her head, takes her hand from his and moves to her mother's side.

Stella stares at me wide-eyed from the carrier. Adam lifts it from his back, smiles at me and says, 'Would you mind holding her while I take off my coat?'

Slowly, the children lose their shyness. I bury myself in their games, trying to ignore the angry voices coming from the kitchen. Adam joins me in the children's room, kneels beside me, saying, 'She'll come round; it won't be forever, I promise.'

Stella is in her high chair. Spaghetti curls festoon her tray. She sports a bolognaise moustache. Ella laughs, 'Stella, you do look funny.'

Adam smiles. 'So do you with sauce on your chin.'

From out of the blue, Alice speaks. 'Kate said you're going back to your old job.'

A small ray of warmth reaches across the table. I catch it before it fades. 'Yes, I start next week. I'm really looking forward to it.'

The curtains are drawn. The room is warm and comfortable. The flickering fire draws us together. We listen to Eva Cassidy singing "Over the Rainbow". 'She has a beautiful voice,' I say.

'The song always makes me feel sad,' says Alice.

'Me too,' I say.

Alice's head is on Adam's shoulder. They're wrapped in the soulful lyrics.

I stand up. 'It's been a long day. I'll say goodnight.'

'Sleep well,' says Adam. 'See you in the morning.'

I stop outside my bedroom door when I hear the softness in her voice, 'Goodnight, Mum.'

Was it the howling wind or the thought of seeing Sean that kept me awake? Alice puts a breakfast bowl onto the draining board. 'When are you seeing Dad?' she asks.

I pick up the bowl and wipe it with the tea towel, thinking about Sean and when and where we will meet.

Alice empties the washing-up water, turns to me, saying, 'You mustn't keep him hanging on. Why not this morning?'

'I've promised to take Ella to the beach.'

'I don't think you'll be there long. There's a storm brewing. I'll give him a ring. I expect he'll pick you up.'

The wind whips our faces, stings our eyes. I pull hair from my mouth and shout, 'Ella, look.' I chase after her, hold her in my arms and point to a sky full of seabirds. We watch their outstretched wings, the effortless, aerial ballet that accompanies the crash of waves. Ella turns my face to hers. I lower my head.

'Granddad!' she shouts, pointing to the sea wall. The solitary figure is as still as a brush stroke, a mere shadow beneath the ominous sky. Pushed by the wind, we follow the drifting sand towards him.

Sean's features are partly hidden by his hood. His figure shrunk in a jacket held tight by his folded arms – I wonder how anybody can change so much in a matter of five months. He looks at Ella. 'Your nana must be mad bringing you here on a day like this. Get in the car; I'll take you home.'

I sit next to Ella – even she is quiet. When she leaves the car, Sean says, 'Tell Mummy we'll see her later.'

'Aren't we going in?'

He turns and looks at me. 'I thought it would be better if we talked privately. We're going to the house.'

'I'd rather go to a pub?'

'I thought pubs were part of your problem,' he says, turning back to the wheel.

The first spatter of rain hits the windscreen. The drops gain momentum, drumming faster and heavier, hitting the road before us, making rivers to the sea. We splash through puddles into the lane and stop outside the house. I scan the yard for Blackie. 'The dog must be staying out of the rain,' I say.

Sean is staring at the veil of water running down the windscreen. 'Did nobody tell you?' he says. 'He's dead, knocked down by a car.'

Before I have time to speak, he's out of the car and in the house. Wondering why nobody told me, I brush away a tear. I try and compose myself – the last thing I want is for Sean to see me crying. These tears are not just for Blackie.

I look at the house. The door is open, waiting for me to go inside. I get out of the car and put my face to the sky, letting the rain fall over me, wanting the sorry mess I've put myself in to be washed clean away.

The first thing I notice when I go into the house is how cold and dark the room is – I resist the urge to put the light on. This is Sean's home now.

Sean is putting the kettle onto a portable gas ring. He turns to look at me. 'What were you doing standing in the rain like that?' He throws me a towel. 'I'm beginning to think you've lost your senses. Someone suggested you might be menopausal.'

I wipe my face and hair, not caring who that someone might be. A shiver goes through me. 'It's cold in here.'

'You shouldn't have stood in the rain. Anyway, there's no point lighting the range, not just for one, and there's the cost of it. Now you've moved into Wellington Road, my income's halved.' He pushes the switch on an electric heater. 'This and the electric blanket has to do. Lily spends all her time in bed now.' He picks up a chair and puts it next to the heater. 'Sit down.'

It's not just the cold that makes the atmosphere depressing; the room speaks of neglect. Next to the gas ring is a frying-pan; in it is a grey sausage, lying in a bed of cold fat. On the table an ash tray spills dog ends. There's not an empty beer tin or wine bottle in sight, and I wonder if he moved them for my approval. He hands me a mug of tea, grabs a chair, sits beside me and rolls a cigarette. Avoiding his gaze, I look down and notice how loose the legs of his jeans are. He inhales. I smell tobacco smoke when he says, 'Anna, look at me.' I lift my head and see the tiredness in his eyes. 'Come home. Things will be different, I promise. You leaving made me realise how much I need you. How much I love you. We'll go for walks, rediscover each other. I'll join AA. There's a group in Ennis. I've made a few calls.'

I remember his promises, all of them broken. The sleepless nights. I only have to look out of the window to see the dent in my car.

'I'll forgive you,' he says. 'David encouraged you. I know he did. You wouldn't have left if it wasn't for him.'

'Maybe not, but I came close to leaving many times.' I take a breath, trying to steady my voice. 'I can't risk being with you and having to do this again. I don't believe your promises.'

Disappointment colours his face. Hurriedly, I say, 'Of course, this is all yours: the house, the furniture, the car.'

Suddenly, he stands up, pushes the chair back, shouting, 'Get out.' He rushes to the door, holds it open. 'I want you gone from my sight.'

I run outside. He follows, saying, 'You can't walk in this weather.' We get into the car and he pushes the gear into first. Ignoring the weather, oncoming traffic, stray dogs, signs, we speed into town. He stops at the crossroads. 'You can walk from here. Tell Alice I'll call in when you've gone.' He turns in the road and in a matter of seconds is out of sight.

CHAPTER 21

'What are you doing for Easter, Anna?'

Maud had been so engrossed in her painting, I'd forgotten she was still in the room. 'I'm going to Ireland; my daughter and grandchildren are there.'

Maud puts her brush into the jam-jar's murky water then sits back into her wheelchair. I put the clay into a bucket, rinse my hands and stand behind her. I look at the cottage scene her arthritic hands had so painfully created. 'Your painting reminds me of Ireland. Though Irish summers are never warm enough or dry enough to produce such colourful and abundant flowers.'

'Well, don't forget to come back,' says Maud, picking up her bag from the table. 'That bloke who left kept interfering; he never shut up, always on about perspective and telling me to use mixed media, whatever that is. I told 'im: I wanna paint, not waste my time talking about it. Not at my age.'

She switches on her wheelchair and puts it into reverse. I step aside. 'Don't worry, I'll be back,' I say, screwing the top onto a messy tube of paint.

Other than a few new service-users and inevitably a few missing, nothing much has changed since I last worked here. Maud's wheelchair gives the door frame a hefty bang and another scratch is added to the scores already there. I get a damp rag and wipe the tables. Vicky makes her customary end of the day visit. 'Thank God, they've gone,' she says. 'I need this break. If I had to pick up Iris's stitches once more I might have stabbed her with one of her knitting-needles. I wish you weren't going away. We could have done something nice.'

'I must go. I want to see Alice and the children.' I put the rag into the bin and look at her. 'We're only just beginning to mend our relationship. I don't want to jeopardise that.'

'How could it? You were only there a couple of weeks ago.'

'Four weeks,' I say. I lock the cupboard door and turn to face her. 'Why don't you and Craig do something? What about Sue and Liz? One of them might be free.'

'Craig's off with his mates playing golf. Sue's staying with her son, and Liz is tied up with a new fella. I suppose it'll be me and the TV.'

I put the key into my desk drawer. 'Things can't be that bad. How are you and Craig getting on?'

'Okay... we hardly see each other. He does all the overtime he can get and it's golf all weekend.'

'Look, when I get back, we'll have a girl's night out.'

'That'll be good. I'm sorry for being such a whinger. What about you? Will you see Sean?' – What can I say? A part of me wants to see him, while the very thought makes me want to run away. Why am I going? As Vicky said, I was there four weeks ago. The trouble is, Sean, Alice, the children are forever on my mind. A picture of Blackie dying on the side of the road haunts me, a fear that if I don't go, something catastrophic will happen. – 'Anna?'

Vicky's voice brings me back to the room. 'Sorry. Yes, Sean. I doubt if I'll see him. There's a few things he has that I want: a ring he gave me, my camera and a necklace that was Mum's. I'm hoping Alice will get them for me.'

'When are you leaving?'

'Tonight. I'm catching the 10 o'clock coach from the bus station, which reminds me, I must get on. I haven't even packed.'

I arrive in Ennis, to a bright sunny day. Adam's waiting at the coach-stop. The bear hug he gives makes me feel welcomed. He's his usual chatty self and when the panoramic view of coast and never-ending sea opens in front of us, we glance at each other, as if to say, there are some good reasons for being here.

Adam parks the car outside the supermarket. He holds the door open for a woman who's pushing a loaded trolley out onto the pavement. She gives him a smile and tightens her grip on the squirming toddler under her arm.

Adam disappears into the shop. I wind down the window. A breath of fresh air brings the cheerful notes of a jig – two men are sat in the sun with pints in their hands, tapping their feet to the music coming from a pub.

The gift shop has dressed its window with brightly coloured plant pots filled with daffodils. Flags, hanging from the awning, flutter a welcome in several different languages

Four back-packers study a map; they part to make way for a child who has come out of the newsagent licking an ice cream. They gather again. One of them points to the road that leads to the beach, and they start walking.

It's not only the balmy day, or the holiday atmosphere that makes me hopeful. The first note of change came soon after I arrived back from work. When the telephone rang and Alice's voice told me Adam would pick me up from Ennis. When she said, 'See you tomorrow' in a way that sounded as though she's happy I'm coming.

Adam comes out of the shop, gets back into the car, saying, 'I'm sorry I've been so long. You wouldn't think Easter would bring such an influx of visitors. Hold onto that.' He puts a bottle of wine onto my lap. 'I thought we'd celebrate your arrival.'

'Come in, Mum. Did you have a good journey?'

Before I have time to answer, Ella runs into the hallway, shouting, 'Nana, play with me?' I pick her up and hold her close – I'm reminded of the weather-house my grandmother once had. On dull days, a little man wearing dark clothes and a sad face came out of the house. On fine days he stayed inside and a girl in a summer dress with bright yellow curls and a huge smile took his place. At this moment, my smile must be every bit as big as that girl's.

I give Ella a kiss on the cheek, put her down, saying, 'Let me take my coat off.' Stella crawls from the lounge. I quickly remove my coat, pick her up and carry her into the kitchen.

Alice is putting a plate of biscuits onto the kitchen table. 'Ella made these,' she says.

Ella looks at me with a serious face. 'You can have as many as you like, Nana, but Stella can only have one. I'm going to get a book and then you can read it to me.'

I sit at the table with Stella on my lap. She starts playing with the necklace I'm wearing. I slip it over my head and give it to her.

'You're looking well,' says Alice, putting a mug of tea next to me.

'Thanks, it's being back at the day-centre, doing a job I like. You look good too.'

'I'm much better. I'd been worried about Dad but, since Diane's been here, he's much happier.'

'Oh, she's in Miltown?'

'Yes, she's been here about a week. She goes back the day after you leave.'

'Are they...?'

'If you mean, are they an item, I think so. She was making moon eyes at him all over Christmas. Dad had been very depressed so I suggested he gave her a call. I thought he needed a bit of female company.'

Ella runs into the room holding a book. I put Stella and the necklace onto the floor, take the book and I open it.

'She's just what Dad needs,' says Alice. 'She's given the place an almighty clean. It had got in a right state. I'd offered to clean it myself but he always said no. Diane wouldn't listen. She's a strong character. I only hope she manages to get him eating more and drinking less.'

I stare down at the book. Ella nudges my arm. 'Nana, are you going to read to me?'

'I'm sorry; Mummy, wants to talk to me. Let me listen to what she's saying.'

'They're having a lovely time. Sight-seeing, walks, they've even been to a few restaurants and you know what Dad's like about...'

Suddenly the necklace breaks. Stella opens her mouth in surprise. Alice and Ella chase beads across the floor. They're about to give them to me when I say, 'Don't worry. They're not worth anything. Gran always said pearls bring tears. Would you like them, Ella? You can paint them – make a necklace of your very own.'

Stella is in her cot. Ella's in her bed, tired from painting, playing and looking at books. I close their door and go to the room where I'm sleeping. I'm about to unzip my case – I've put the little brown case, the memories it holds, away in my attic – when l think about Sean and admit the jealousy I feel is entirely unreasonable.

Adam pours three glasses of wine. Alice places a beef casserole onto the table and says, 'Thanks, Mum. All that playing tired them out.'

'There's no need for thanks; I enjoyed it.' I wait for a moment before saying, 'There's a few things I want from the house: my camera, a necklace that was Nan's and a ring Sean gave me. Would you mind going there and getting them for me?'

Alice has tried to get in touch with Sean a number of times. She's beginning to think they've gone away for a few days. She has a key and offered to collect my things for me. She wants to know where to find them. At one time I could have told her where everything is, but they may have been moved. Now she wants me to go with her. I worry that Sean and Diane will arrive while we're there. I'm not ready to see him with someone else.

We reach the top of Lasheen Hill. I keep my head bowed as we drive past Mary's and Bridie's bungalows. I never even said goodbye.

Sean's old Ford is parked in the yard. The Cinquecento is nowhere to be seen. The flower beds need weeding.

The house is clean and tidy. The same table sits in the middle of the kitchen. The same curtains hang at the windows – I am the stranger.

Lily is asleep next to the range. The range is warm. Someone lit a fire this morning.

Alice whispers, 'Be quick.'

I run up the stairs. The bed is neatly made. The ash tray has been taken away.

I open the top drawer of the dressing-table and take out my camera, feel beneath jumpers and find the necklace in its box. I open the bottom drawer and put my hand right to the back. There it is: a small velvet, drawstring bag. I bring it out, look inside and slip it into my pocket. I'm about to leave when I notice a blue plastic bottle next to the bed. I pick it up. 'FEMAX... for comfortable penetration.'

Alice's voice calls, 'Mum! They're here!'

I throw the bottle onto the bed. By the time I reach the bottom step, Sean's in the kitchen. He points his finger at me and looks at Alice, 'Why's she here?'

I try and answer for her. 'I came to pick up...'

He turns to me. 'Shut up. You've no right in this house!'

'Dad, please. Mum needed to get a few things'.

'Get her out, Alice. Get her out before I throw her out'.

'Come on, Mum. Have you got what you were looking for? I'll ring you later, Dad. After you've calmed down.'

I follow her outside. Diane sits in the Cinquecento, as still as a statue, an ice queen, as we drive away.

CHAPTER 22

The news calls for a sit-down, so I take the phone to the stairs and place myself on the bottom step.

'...We gave the tenant a month's notice yesterday,' says Alice. 'We should be back around mid-May.'

'Why? What made you decide so suddenly?'

'Things haven't panned out the way we'd hoped. Adam's had no work, not to speak of, since we arrived. You know what they're like here. Everybody knows somebody who knows somebody who's a plumber.'

'What about Sean? He's going to miss you.'

'Dad's not here. He's at Diane's.'

'At Diane's! You'd told me he'd gone to Bristol, but I didn't realise he was still here.'

'Yes. He hates being on his own. He did come back, but only briefly to pick up the cat.'

'The cat! How long's he here for?'

'I don't know. As long as he wants.'

'What does Kate think? Have you told her?'

'What, about us coming back? She's thrilled and, like me, she's glad Dad's got Diane. He needs looking after. His drinking has taken a real toll on his health.'

'Kate said nothing to me about Sean being here.'

'That's because when she mentions Dad you always look so sad... Look Mum, we want you to be happy, to get on with your life and leave Dad to get on with his.'

'What you're saying is right and I know I'm being unfair. But... at the moment... it's just that... I need to adjust... it takes a little time getting used to the fact he's with someone else.'

'Anyway, are you glad we're coming back?'

'Of course, and you'll be so near.'

Stella starts to scream. 'I must go,' says Alice.

'Don't forget to let me know if there's anything I can do. And I'm really excited about you coming home.'

Thinking about Sean and Diane, I put the phone down. Diane's house is no more than a twenty-minute walk away. I'm bound to see them sometime. We probably use the same supermarket.

CHAPTER 23

Liz's voice is drowned out by the rock band's screaming voices and the crash of drums. I try to shout above the noise then shake my head. Liz points across the room and we skirt our way around the excited audience. I follow her through a door, up a flight of steps and out onto a patio. After taking a breath of cool, clean air, I say, 'I don't think I could've stood there a minute longer.'

The patio is deserted. We make our way to a table and I ask, 'What were you trying to say?'

'I wanted to know how Alice is. Is she back?'

'Yes, they came back sooner than expected. The tenants were planning to leave anyway and were happy with a fortnight's notice. They're all well. In fact, I'm seeing them tomorrow. Alice has invited me and Kate to lunch.'

We hear Sue's voice call, 'We thought we'd find you here.'

We look behind us. Vicky gives a wave. 'God! It's good to be out of there,' she says, sitting down beside me.

Sue kicks off her white stilettos, saying, 'These shoes are killing me. I think my clubbing days are over.'

'Mine too,' agrees Vicky. 'It's the noise I can't stand.'

'Bring back the sixties,' I say, nostalgically remembering the Carpenters and Dusty Springfield. 'At least there was a tune and you could understand what they're singing about.'

'I agree,' says Sue, massaging her feet. 'I like a place where you can sit comfortably and you don't have to queue for the loo. I hate to say it, but my days of noisy bars and dancing around are long gone. Next time we have a girl's night out, let's go somewhere where we can hear each other talk.'

'Trouble is,' says Liz, 'pubs and clubs are like that. You can't get away from it. Just wait and see what happens when that band stops playing. They'll be out here, pissed out of their minds. If you want somewhere quiet, we'll have to go out of town, which means, as Sue is the only one with a car, she'll have to drive, or it's taxis, and that'll be expensive.'

Suddenly, Sue sits up and, forgetting her feet, exclaims, 'I know, what about a girls' weekend away? I've a cousin who has a holiday cottage in Devon. It's in a lovely village, a few miles from Woolacombe. I'm sure she wouldn't mind us using it. We'd have to pay her.'

'Of course,' says Vicky. 'That won't be a problem.'

'Mike's starting to get his feet stuck under my table,' says Liz. 'Me going away without him might give the message that I'm a girl who likes her freedom.'

I look at Sue. 'You can count me in.'

'Good, that's the four of us. I'll give her a ring tomorrow.'

'Here they come,' says Liz.

Within minutes the patio is heaving with people. A young girl falls against our table. A man shouts, 'God, Trixie, you can't be pissed already; it's only nine-thirty. What you gonna be like at kick-out?'

'Dead,' laughs another man as he helps her to her feet.

Liz stands up, saying, 'Get your shoes on, Sue. Let's get out of here. Mike left a couple of bottles of wine at my place. Let's go and plan our trip.'

I wake up to a headache; a stream of light is coming through the window. I glance at the clock: I've got a couple of hours before I leave for Alice's.

I didn't think I'd had that much to drink – a gin in the pub, and the four of us shared two bottles of wine, though it was a large gin and Sue hardly touched the wine. You'd think I'd want to stay away from the stuff. I was always so anti. Hated the sight of the bottles lined along the dresser. Mrs

Sensible, that's what Sean called me. Well, he wouldn't have said that if he'd seen me last night, four giggling women planning a trip to Devon. All of us feeling very "Thelma and Louise". It was gone two when Vicky, Sue and I finally climbed into a taxi.

The walk to Alice's is along an old railway track, now a cycle path. A fine Saturday has brought out people of all ages – dog walkers, joggers, cyclists and those who fancy a stroll. Hawthorn blooms amongst the bushes and trees that edge the path, clusters of cream flowers perfume the air. The prospect of going away, the fragrance of early summer clear my head, put a spring in my step. I stop when I get to the exit to Greenway Road. From here, a ten-minute walk will take me to Diane's house. I think about Sean, wondering what he's doing, if he and Diane ever walk this path and what I'd do if I met them.

The Sunday visit to Alice and her family, in many ways, is as it has always been – Alice's welcome kiss on my cheek, Kate's smile that reminds me of her father, the smell of roasting meat, the dinner service Sean and I gave for a wedding present, the lace tablecloth that was my mother's – no one mentions the person who's missing and who the culprit is.

Ella is holding her sister's hand. Stella points to her new shoes. I admire them and congratulate her on her walking. Adam takes the high chair into the dining room. We sit for lunch. The conversation centres round the children. Adam plays aeroplanes to encourage Stella to eat. He tells the children, 'If you finish your food, I'll take you to the park and buy you an ice cream.' It doesn't take long before Ella's plate is empty, and Adam is putting Stella into her buggy.

I stand up from the table, saying, 'I'll give you a hand with the washing up.'

'I'll do it later,' says Alice. 'You and Kate go and sit in the lounge. I'll make coffee.'

I relax into an armchair. Kate is standing with her back to me, looking out of the window.

'It's been such lovely weather,' I say. 'Let's hope it continues.'

Alice comes into the room; Kate turns away from the window as Alice puts a tray onto the coffee table. The girls glance at each other and Kate says, 'Mum, Dad rang last night. He wants to ask you a favour.'

I sit up. 'Me? Why? What does he want?'

'He wants you to have Lily.'

'Lily! Why? He dotes on her.'

'Diane's cat and Lily don't get on,' says Kate. 'She told Dad that Lily has to go.'

'It's early days,' I say. 'It'll take a little while, but they'll get used to each other.'

'That's what I said,' says Kate, 'but Diane's adamant. Lily has to go. I'd have her myself but my landlady doesn't allow pets.'

'I thought about it as well,' says Alice, 'but you know what Lily's like; she hates children, and Stella will terrorise her.'

'Dad asked Chris,' says Kate, but she said Granddad's forever chasing cats out of the garden; the last thing he'll want is a cat in the house.'

'So, it's down to me,' I say. 'The last resort.'

'Dad knows you'll take good care of her,' says Kate.

I take a deep breath. 'All right, I suppose so. Me and the girls are planning a weekend away, but I'm sure Blodwyn won't mind feeding her.'

'If she can't do it, I will,' says Alice.

'Okay. Give Sean my number; tell him to give me a call. I'm home all evening.'

I quickly open the door, shut it and grab the phone. 'Sean!' I say. 'I didn't expect you to ring this soon. I've only just got in.'

'I'm sorry. Kate said...'

'Yes, she told me. You want me to have Lily. I'm in most evenings. Let me know when you're coming and I'll...'

'It needs to be now.'

'Now! Can't it wait? I'm not ready. I haven't anything for her.'

'I've got all that. It's in the car. I'm in Wellington Road. Kate said you'd be home by now. Look Anna, I'm sorry, but...'

'Well, you'd better come in.'

I put the phone down and within minutes there's a knock on the door. Straight away I notice his thinning hair, his eyes tinged with yellow, his clothes hanging on his body. The shock of seeing him looking so ill leaves me with an ache that longs to hold him.

Lily gives a wail of distress. Sean follows me into the kitchen and puts the pet-carrier onto the table. Lily's cries get louder. Sean looks at her through the bars, saying, 'You'll be out soon.' He turns to me. 'I've her cushion and cat food in the car. I won't be a minute.'

I close the kitchen door and lift Lily from her prison. Her claws hook onto my T shirt. Muttering words of comfort, I hold her tight.

Sean returns with a cushion and a large bag, puts them on the floor then gently unhooks Lily from me. He cradles her in his arms, saying, 'Thanks, Anna. I didn't know what else to do.'

'There's no need for thanks. She'll be no trouble and you can always visit. Maybe you'd like to try her with Diane's cat again. If you gradually introduce them, they may get to...'

~ 185 ~

'No, I don't think I'll be doing that.' He gives a nervous laugh. 'I haven't told the girls, but she hasn't only thrown Lily out, she told me to go as well.'

'Oh, I'm sorry. So where are you going?'

'To Dad's, just until I sort myself out. I...'

He stops speaking. Our unsaid words caught in a web of thoughts and emotions. I break the silence. 'Would you like a drink? Tea? Coffee?'

'No, I won't stop. Chris is making one of her gigantic meals. I must be going.'

'Give them my love. The girls keep me updated. Tell them...' I stop what I'm about to say – that it's shame that stops me from being in touch.'

Sean looks at Lily, strokes her and asks, 'Where would you like me to put her?'

'In the sitting room. I'll keep the door shut. I'm going to be in and out of the garden; I wouldn't want to lose her.'

I wait in the hallway. When Sean comes out of the sitting-room, he puts his hand in his pocket, saying, 'I'll leave you some money.'

'There's no need for that.'

He gives a sad smile. 'Thanks – if you're sure.'

I open the door. We stand on the threshold. 'Are you receiving the rent money?' I ask. 'Kate said she was sorting it out and is sending you a cheque each month.'

'Yes, she is. And your car, I...'

'Keep it. I'm doing quite all right without one.'

He nods. 'Thanks. I must be going.'

He walks to the gate. The urge to call him back, to ask him to stay, is overwhelming.' He steps onto the pavement and, ignoring my heart, I let him disappear from sight.

CHAPTER 24

Blodwyn never ceases to amaze me. Morning, noon or night, she looks as though she's going to a party, and this evening is no exception. From her lacquered platinum blonde hair, right down to her gold platform sandals, she's dressed to impress. She stands in my kitchen like a neat little Barbie doll, her mini skirt startling white against her fake tan legs. She gives me a dazzling smile and lifts the hem of her shocking pink top. 'What do you think?' she asks.

I look at the pink jewel in her navel, wondering how to reply.

'D'you like it?'

'It suits your outfit. It's quite striking.'

She gives a big smile. 'They come in all colours. You should think about getting one; they're all the fashion.'

Hastily changing the subject, I go to the kitchen cupboard, open it, saying, 'Thanks for feeding Lily. The cat food's in here. Give her half a tin twice a day and water, not milk – it makes her sick.' I hand her the key. 'I'll be back Sunday. When you feed her in the morning leave the key on the table.' I point to a note pad. 'I've written Alice's number, just in case, but I'm sure Lily won't be any trouble.'

'Is Sean in Bristol?' she asks.

Her question makes me wary. 'Why do you want to know?'

'I thought I saw 'im. Trev was with me and I said, I'm sure that's Anna's Sean. It was 'is spitting image, though thinner than I remember. 'e was with a woman.'

She waits for me to say something.

'I haven't seen him since he brought Lily. He said he was staying with his dad. He might be in Bristol; he has a friend here.'

'If it was Sean, 'e's awfully thin. Where's 'is friend live?' She sits at the table, crosses her legs as though ready to stay a while.

'Sorry, Blodwyn. I haven't time to talk. Sue's going to be here and I've got things to do.'

'I must go too,' says Blodwyn, standing up. 'Trev'll wonder where 'is dinner is.'

I follow her to the door. ''ave a lovely time' she says. 'If you ever want a natter, I'll always listen and I won't breathe a word, cross me heart.'

'I will, and thanks Blodwyn.'

I haven't seen or heard from Sean since the day he brought Lily. Alice and Kate told me over a week ago that he's back with Diane. Knowing how much he loves Lily, I expected him to visit.

I go to my bedroom. Lily is on the bed; she hasn't moved since I left for work this morning. I sit next to her, feeling the vibration of her purr against my hand. There's so much I don't understand about myself. I was always against Lily sharing our bed. Now I'm pleased to see her, find myself calling her name, wanting her little body next to mine.

I leave Lily and concentrate on what I'm supposed to be doing. Sue's cousin has asked us to bring our own sheets and towels. I pull the case from under the bed, pack it with bedding and anything else I might need. Downstairs, I put on my jacket and wait at the window for Sue's car to appear.

'If the traffic's good we should be at the cottage by nine,' says Sue. 'We'll pick Liz up first, and Vicky on the way to the motorway. How was she today?'

I think back to this morning when I found her crying in the staff toilets. 'Still upset but looking forward to getting away.'

'I wish she could see Craig for what he is,' says Sue. 'I've suspected him of playing around for a long time.'

What can I say? Who am I to make comments about Craig's indiscretions.

A chorus of bird song wakes me. I don't know what the time is; there's no clock in the room and I left my phone at home. I glance at Liz. She is fast asleep. I sit up, looking around me. The room is charming, furnished with the old type of utility furniture I remember from my childhood. Faded wallpaper covers uneven walls, bare floorboards and a wooden latch door reminds me of the house in Ireland.

I leave the bed and go to the bathroom. A blue gingham curtain hangs at the window. I shift it aside and push down the sash. Last night's rain has left an energizing smell of wet grass. A gap between two beech trees gives a glimpse of rooftops and distant hills, the cry of a cockerel beckons.

I get dressed and creep down the stairs. In the living room are the remnants from last night – two empty wine bottles, crumpled crisp packets and an empty chocolate box, memorabilia of a night of congeniality that sent Vicky to bed knowing she has her friends' support.

I go out onto the street. Curtains are drawn, shutters closed, cars rest in silence on cobbled driveways. Other than bird song and a black cat slinking into the hedgerow, the village is deserted.

The clock on the church tower says twelve, but what twelve that might be I don't know; yesterday, last year, or has time stood still? I open the church gate and close it behind me. Some of the gravestones have shifted position, forwards, backwards, to the side, as though they had been part of a macabre dance. A few have fallen, covering the grave in a final clinch.

I wander along the path, stopping every so often to read the name on a gravestone. I find myself next to a low stone wall. Beyond the wall is a field dotted with sheep. A few have made their way into the churchyard and are chomping at the short springy grass. I sit on the wall and read the lettering on Isaac Hayman and his wife Hannah's grave. Isaac died in June 1895 at the age of eighty-seven; his wife Hannah was eighty-six when she followed him the following September. I wonder if they'd had a happy marriage, if temptation ever got in their way.

I think about Vicky – Sue's probably right in her summing-up of Craig – Vicky won't believe this, but she will get over the upset. She's the innocent. It's the likes of me and Craig that suffer. We're the ones who discover that when love disappears, guilt takes its place.

I gaze into the distance, lost in a pool of regrets, not moving until I hear the church gate open. A woman appears, carrying flowers. She gives me a smile. Unable to bear the kindness in her eyes – I nod my head and walk away.

'Here she is. We were wondering where you were,' says Sue.

The three of them are sat at the kitchen table. Liz is painting her fingernails in characteristic pillar box red. Vicky gives a brief smile and resumes texting. 'Do you want a cup of tea?' asks Sue. Without waiting for a reply, she picks up the teapot and pours me one.

'I woke up early,' I say, sitting down. 'It was such a lovely morning, I went for a stroll in the village.'

'We were just discussing what we're going to do,' says Sue.

Vicky closes her phone and puts it into her bag, saying, 'I haven't been sleeping well. I wouldn't mind a walk, then perhaps a snooze in the sun.'

'Sounds good to me,' says Liz, admiring her nails.

'I'd like to look at the sea,' I say.

'What about Woolacombe?' asks Sue. 'It's got a lovely beach and it's only a short drive away.'

'I went to Woolacombe years ago,' I say. 'Sean and I were staying in Ilfracombe, a coastal town not far from here. Someone told me Woolacombe beach is three miles long.' – I don't tell them I'd wanted to walk the length of that beach. That Sean preferred the pub and that's where we stayed.

I walk the length of Woolacombe beach, thinking about Sean, wishing I'd encouraged him to have walked this glorious beach with me. When I return, the others are asleep in the sun. I join them. None of us are brave enough to get into the sea.

We go back to the cottage with pink faces and sand in our hair. It only takes a quick shower, putting on make-up and a change of clothes, to send us to the village pub. An evening of good wine and food eventually drives us to our beds.

Something wakes me. My eyes are wide open, my body as tight as a string on a bow. The thud of my heart beats a message. It tells me that Sean is in serious danger. I lay awake, staring into the dark for what seems like hours, before falling into a maze of troubled dreams. I wake with the dawn, still anxious, still convinced I'd received a premonition.

I don't notice that Liz is awake until she says, 'Are you alright?'

'Yes,' I say, trying to smile.

'You're very quiet.'

'I was wishing we could stay a bit longer,' I lie.

This feeling of dread clings to me, is with me every moment: through our chatter, our wander through Barnstaple, the drive home. It's with me when we say goodbye, all the time gathering force. I put my key in the latch, step into my house, knowing something is about to happen, yet I still jump when I see Kate, white-faced, standing in the kitchen doorway.

'I've been trying to ring you all day,' she says, her anxiety spilling into anger. 'You must remember to take your phone with you!'

'Tell me what's happened?'

'It's Dad. He's in hospital. He's been asking for you. He's dying. He might not last the night.'

CHAPTER 25

I'm not surprised to see Kate. The premonition never left me. I drop my luggage onto the floor and ask, 'What's wrong with him?'

'He has pancreatic cancer.' She picks up her keys. 'He's been asking for you. Let's go.'

We leave the house; within seconds we're in her car. She starts the engine, pulls away from the kerb, and accelerates down the road. She stops at the junction, looks left and right, saying, 'When you didn't answer your phone I was frantic, then I remembered Alice has a key.' She makes a dash across the road, narrowly missing a white van.

'Where's Alice?' I ask, nervously watching the speedometer.

'At the hospital.'

'When was he admitted?'

'This morning; Diane took him. They'd gone to Ireland for a break. While they were there he became increasingly ill and...' She stops speaking and I look at her. 'He looks terrible, like a skeleton. And his skin! I've never seen anything like it! It's yellow, even the whites of his eyes are yellow.'

We come to a roundabout. I wait until we're on the dual carriageway before asking, 'When did they come back?'

'Yesterday. Diane could see he was seriously ill. They took the overnight ferry. They had a horrendous journey. Getting him out of the car and up into a cabin took enormous effort. When they disembarked she drove like mad. By the time they arrived at the hospital Dad was unconscious. She thought he was dead and ran for help. He was admitted straight away.'

My mind goes back to last night; they would have been on the ferry when the premonition woke me.

I ask myself, why had I been so neglectful? My eyes were telling me Sean had been losing weight and foolishly I put it down to him not eating properly. It was only a few weeks ago when Lily came to live with me, when I'd looked at Sean and saw how wretched and unhappy he was. I chose to believe he looked that way because he was missing me. I'd ignored my instinct to put my arm around him and ask him to stay because... I can't lie to myself; the truth is the grievances I carry are like pebbles in my pocket and I can't let them go.

We pass a sign directing us to the hospital. The open gates loom ahead. We drive through them and stop in the car park, wait with agonising impatience for a driver to comb her hair, adjust her seat belt and leave the parking space. I'd come without my purse. Kate searches for change and I hurry to the meter.

We move quickly through the grounds. The hospital door automatically opens. People part as we hurry towards the lift. The lift door closes. We rush to the stairs, our feet drumming a percussion of steps to the second floor. Ward Thirteen – an ominous number. Kate knows the procedure. She presses a bell. A woman's voice, a buzz from the door allows us into the ward. Kate gestures towards a plastic bottle attached to the wall. I rub the blue liquid into my hands and see Chris, her face pale and worried, walking towards us. We cling together and fears that she will be hostile evaporate. 'I'm glad you came,' she says; 'he keeps asking for you.'

'Where's Alice?'

'You just missed her. She needed to get home.'

'And Bill, is he here?'

'Yes, he and Diane are with Sean.' Chris looks at Kate. My heart gives a leap of hope when Chris says, 'The doctor came this afternoon. They're going to operate.'

We follow Chris into a small room; a jumble of torn magazines and the smell of sneaked cigarettes leave prints of anxious family, friends and lovers.

Kate and I look at Chris, desperate for good news. 'They're operating first thing tomorrow morning,' she says.

'Then he'll be alright,' I say, putting words into her mouth.

She shakes her head. 'No, people with pancreatic cancer have few symptoms. By the time it's diagnosed it will have spread. Surgery will give some relief. It may help prolong his life. Sean's bile duct is obstructed by the tumour. They're going to insert a stent to keep it open. It will help reduce the jaundice.'

'But surely,' I say, 'there are other treatments. What about chemotherapy?'

'I'm as much in the dark as you are. The doctor said the prognosis is very poor. Most people don't survive the year.'

The guilt I feel is unbearable. If I hadn't left him, if I'd been with him, I would have noticed his decline. He would have received treatment sooner.

I hear myself say, 'How is Alice?'

'Very upset,' says Chris. 'She wanted to get home and be with Adam and the children.' She stands up from her chair. 'I'll tell Sean you're here.'

Diane, Chris and Bill walk towards us. Bill's eyes are red from crying. He takes my hand and I kiss his cheek. I look at Diane, wondering what I should say. It's a relief when she turns her head away.

'Where is he?' I ask.

Chris points towards a brightly patterned screen and says, 'In the far corner.' I leave them and walk towards it.

Sean's skin is the colour of mustard, his lashes lying like blackbird's feathers on closed eyelids. Trying not to disturb him, I pick up a chair, move it to his bed, and sit beside him. We are in a world of our own, the sounds from the ward diminished to some other place, my fear for him, filling every corner.

Sean's eyelashes flutter. He stares at the ceiling, turns his head towards me, looks at me with big yellow eyes, saying, 'It's all yours now, Anna: the houses, our savings, all of it is yours.'

The air is heavy with the finality of his words. I try and banish the oppression with a joke, something I know he will appreciate. 'I bet you're glad you didn't pay the tax you owe.' He smiles and I say, 'Anyway you're not gone yet and they're operating tomorrow.'

'I'm dying,' he says. 'I always knew I'd die young and I don't regret a thing. Not a thing.'

His words fill me with sadness. I want to say, 'Not a thing. Not even us. That it might have been different.'

He returns his gaze to the ceiling, saying, 'I wanted to say goodbye.'

'I'll come again tomorrow, after your operation. If you're too tired, perhaps the next day. I can call any time. Whenever you...'

'No, Anna. I don't want to see you again.'

CHAPTER 26

'Jenny, it's Anna.'

'Anna, I didn't recognise your voice. This is a nice surprise. No work today?'

'No... I... I didn't go in... I...'

'What's the matter? You sound upset.'

'Something dreadful's happened.'

'What is it? What's the matter?'

'It's Sean. He's terribly ill. He's dying!'

'Dying! Of what? What's happened?'

'Cancer. They say it's terminal... and... I'm sorry... I can't seem to stop crying.'

'Oh Anna... Shh.'

'I needed to talk to you, Jenny.'

'That's what sisters are for.'

'I feel terrible.'

'Well, it's all so sudden. When was he taken ill?'

'It's been coming on a long time... I just didn't... Jenny... What have I done?'

'What do you mean? What have you done?'

'It's my fault. If I hadn't left him...'

'Don't be silly. How can it be your fault?'

'If I hadn't left, if I'd been there, he wouldn't have become ill and...'

'Anna! People get cancer. It's nobody's fault. I'm sure Sean will tell you the same...'

'He won't see me. I saw him yesterday and he told me he didn't want to see me again.'

'Why? Why did he say that?'

'Because he hates me. Because I left him and now he's dying.'

'Anna! Stop it. I want you to pack a bag and come to me. Do it now!'

'No, I can't. I need to be here in case he changes his mind, in case he needs me.'

'Liz, it's Anna.'

'Hi, you're back from work early.'

'I've had some really bad news.'

'Hang on a minute, let me get my coffee. I've just got in myself... Fire away.'

'Sean's got cancer.'

'Cancer! When. Who told you?'

'Kate; when I got back yesterday she was here. She took me to the hospital.'

'That was sudden. What a shock. Try not to worry. More and more people are recovering from it and...'

'Not this one. Pancreatic cancer is terminal.'

'I'm so sorry. How is he?'

'Terrible. He looked terrible. They're operating today. It'll relieve some of the symptoms but it won't save him...'

'Would you like a lift to the hospital? I'm sure Mike will let me use his...'

'I'm not going to the hospital. He doesn't want to see me. I'll never see him again. I won't be there when he...'

'Shh, don't cry. He'll change his mind. I'm sure he'll...'

'He won't. He doesn't want me near him. I don't blame him. What I did was despicable. And with David of all people. I hate myself. The stress I gave him was terrible. Stress can cause cancer. Did you know that?'

'Anna! Stop beating yourself up. I'm coming round to see you.'

'No, please. I've a dreadful headache. I need to lie down. The girls might call in; they're going to let me to know how the operation went.'

'Anna, it's Sue. Liz told me about Sean.'

'Sorry, Sue. I can't talk for long. The girls are going to ring.'

'I wanted you to know that if there's anything I can do, you only have to ask.'

'There's not much anyone can do, but thanks.'

'I'm sure Sean will change his mind. He'll want to see you.'

'I hope you're right. But I must say goodbye.'

'Eve, it's Anna. I'm going to have to cancel this evening.'

'Oh, that's a shame. I was looking forward to it. I hope nothing's the matter?'

'Sean's in hospital. He's been diagnosed with pancreatic cancer. Alice and Kate are going to call in after they've seen him.'

'Tut, that's all you hear these days... cancer, cancer, but try not to worry; more and more people get over it. The recovery rate is far higher than it used to be.'

'People don't recover from pancreatic cancer.'

'Oh, I'm sorry. You must be very upset.'

'I am. I didn't go to work yesterday or today.'

'I understand. Don't worry. We can always arrange another evening. Let me know how you are. If you fancy a chat, just give me a call.'

'Thanks, Eve, I will.'

The phone wakes me. I push myself up from the sofa and grab my mobile. Seeing David's name, I press delete.

The doorbell rings. I rush to the door and open it. David puts his foot on the threshold. Before I can stop him, he's in the house.

'GET OUT!' My anger bounces across the narrow passageway.

'Anna! I want to talk. Eve told me Sean...'

His voice, his presence, amplifies my guilt. 'GET OUT!'

I run into the kitchen. He chases after me, saying, 'Not until you tell me how Sean is.' He opens his arms. 'Anna, please.'

I look around me. There's no escape. David and I can be on opposite ends of a desert. Be in different continents, and still our sin connects us.

He steps towards me.

'DON'T TOUCH ME!'

He puts his arms down. 'Eve told me. She said Sean...'

'Yes, he's dying and it's our fault. While we were fucking, his cancer was growing and it's too late to do anything about it.'

My heart beats with the speed of a racehorse. 'Please go,' I beg.

'I will, but first tell me which hospital he's in.'

'No. He won't see you. He hates us.'

'I'll find out easily enough.' He turns away. I listen to his footsteps leave the house.

I sit with my head resting on my arm. Grief flows in a deluge of tears. A hand touches my shoulder. A woman's voice, soft and concerned, says, 'Oh babe,' and I look up into Blodwyn's black mascara-fringed eyes. 'I heard shouting,' she says. The door was open so I came in. When you're ready I'll make us a nice cuppa.'

CHAPTER 27

I don't tell her everything, not the whole truth. How can I? Blodwyn's dress may be bordering risqué but she's no strumpet; honesty shines through her fake tan and heavy make-up. I keep my head down, staring at one red square on the checked table cloth, not daring to meet her gaze, not wanting to see my guilt reflected in her eyes. I tell her only what I think she might find acceptable; shame allows me to relate only one small part of the story.

I tell her I left Sean because he was an alcoholic, that I'd felt isolated without the support of family and friends. I don't tell her Alice had moved to be near us. I lie when I say David and I started a relationship after I moved back to England and when we realised how wrong it was we decided to part.

What a coward and a cheat I am. In her innocence she believes the yarn I spin. Holds my hand and listens quietly when I tell her how ill Sean is and that he won't see me because another woman's at his bedside.

When I finally lift my head and tell her it was David that I had been shouting at, she tuts and says, 'You made a mistake but that was then and now's now.'

She walks to the kettle, switches it on, turns back towards me, saying in a voice as resolute as a commander going to battle, 'I wouldn't take no for an answer; I'd be there with 'im all the way. I'm telling you, if it were my Trev I'd be telling that bloody woman to sling 'er 'ook.' She takes two mugs from the shelf and, throwing a tea bag into each, says, 'Nobody knows my Trev like I do. I know 'im inside out: what 'e likes to eat, what 'e watches on telly. When you've been together that long you know you're the best person to look after 'em. Not some stranger who's waltzed into 'is life and thinks she knows everything.' She puts the tea onto the table, then taking my hand she looks at me in earnest. Her eyes hold me. Her voice full of conviction tells me, 'If you love 'im, you'll fight tooth and nail for 'im.'

I sip at my tea, listening to her chatter. When we finish drinking she bustles around clearing the table and washing the cups. Her cheery 'Bye, see you later' leaves me feeling positive with hope.

When Kate and Alice arrive from the hospital, Blodwyn's fighting spirit is still with me. They tell me the operation went well, glance at each other before saying Sean doesn't want to see me. I look them in the eye, saying, 'I respect Sean's wishes but there are other ways to keep in touch. I'll write regularly and often. I won't let him forget me.' Saying the words out loud strengthens my resilience. One way or another I'm going to remind him I'm here, that my door is always open to him.

I've taken another day's sick-leave. Rushing from work to catch the card shop before it closes is not an option. Choosing a card is going to be a long and tricky business – I look at pictures of tranquil beaches, gardens, bluebell woods, sunsets, boats, romantic pastels, mists and sunsets, rivers and seas. Knowing Sean won't want to be reminded of places he'll never see again, I go to another section: "Where's granddad's balls?... In his underpants where they always are." The endless vulgar jokes are not for Sean.

I'm wondering if I'm ever going to find what I'm looking for when I spot a display of black and white cards. I pick one up. Surgeons are gathered around an operating table, the caption reads: "The operation was a success. They managed to remove the £5 note from dad's wallet". Picturing the rise of a smile on Sean's face, I go to the counter.

I take my find to a café. I've come prepared – pen, paper, stamp. I ponder on what to write – *I hope you're feeling better*? How better and for how long? *Glad to hear the operation was successful*. Only a cure can have the congratulations of success. In the end I write: *I'm glad the operation has made you more comfortable, Love Anna*.

I wonder about the word "love", if he will think it rolled from my tongue like ink from the pen. But I tuck love into the card, hoping he will find it.

Taking more than three days off work requires a doctor's note. I know I must go back but what I don't want is the undeserved sympathy, the questions that might be asked. When I rang Margaret in tears, she told me to take some time off until I felt better. Will I ever feel better? Anyway, I can't hang around watching television with Lily forever. It's not good for either of us. With reluctance, I put Lily onto the floor and set the alarm for seven.

Vicky is the first person I see. She hurries into my room, ten minutes late, her face drawn and tired. 'Sue told me about Sean,' she says. 'I'm so sorry. I would have rung but I've been rather upset myself.'

'Why, what's happened?'

'Craig has left me. He has someone else.'

I put my arms around her, too ashamed to look her in the eye – Craig and I are two of a kind.

I hear the clients come grumbling into the room. Leaving Vicky, I go over to them.

'That tea they gave us was stone cold,' says Maud.

'Like dishwater,' says Vera.

'I'd better go,' says Vicky. 'Mine'll be wondering where I am.'

I watch her leave then take the keys from my desk. I'm about to open the pottery cupboard when I hear a beep from my phone. Kate's name appears. I read her message – *David came 2 hospital. R u still seeing him? Tell him 2 stay away!*

I quickly reply: *No. Eve must have told him.*
Tell Eve 2 tell him 2 stay away from Dad and us all.

I scour card shops. When I can't find anything suitable, I write letters. I write funny stories about my clients. Amusing conversations I've had with Blodwyn. Some of the stories are untrue; I've seen tiddlers in the stream near my house, but never a trout. Nor has Lily caught a rat.

The girls visit Sean most evenings. They say my cards are never on display. There are no letters in his bedside cabinet. He never mentions my name.

Both girls are exhausted. I do my best to make life easier for them – cooking meals, baby-sitting. I'm giving Ella a bedtime drink when I hear Alice and Kate come into the house. They stand at the sitting-room door. 'How is he?' I ask.

'He's going home tomorrow,' says Kate.

'Home?' A quick glance from one to the other answers my question.

'Diane's,' says Alice.

CHAPTER 28

Margaret finishes speaking and a hush falls across the room. For a few seconds her sudden announcement hangs in the air. We stare at her, all of us trying to make sense of what has just been said. Then the reticent looks, the agitated whispers breathing unease around the room.

'What?'

'When?'

'Do you remember there was talk of closing the centre a few years ago?'

Margaret holds up her hands. 'Quiet. I'm sorry to bring bad news but a decision has been made. I've been told we won't be taking any new clients in the future.'

'How long have we got?' calls a voice from behind me.

'Twelve months at the most. I think by next summer the centre will be gone.' Her ample nylon-clad bosom heaves a sigh and she says, 'I'll update you as soon as I have more information. You're going to be late getting home tonight. I'll make sure you all get an hour's overtime.'

She turns, walks towards the door, stops when she comes to where I'm sitting. 'Anna, when you're ready, come and see me in my office.'

Margaret leaves the room. Vicky looks at me, saying, 'Wonder what she wants you for.'

'I don't know. Maybe she's going to get rid of me. I'm the latest recruit and I haven't got a contract.'

People are starting to leave. We join them and I wonder how I'm going to manage without a wage.

We stop outside Margaret's office. 'After news like that,' says Vicky, 'I need a drink. Do you fancy going to Bianco's?'

'Yes, though I don't know how long Margaret will keep me.'

'Don't worry. I'll save you a seat. See you there.'

Thinking about Vicky and past events, I make my way to the office. It seems a lifetime since I last sat in Bianco's. Vicky would have been cursing Craig's latest indiscretion. I'd be moaning about Sean drinking too much. Now we're without the men that troubled us, are we any happier? I'm certainly not. Vicky has the best chance of moving on.

I give a tap on the office door. Margaret calls, 'Come in,' and looks at me over the rim of her glasses. She puts the papers she's reading aside. 'Ah, Anna, sit down. I want to talk to you about the pottery.' She removes her glasses, puts them on her desk, saying, 'The powers above have told me it has to close. As from tomorrow, the pottery is out of bounds.'

I'm shocked. I didn't expect the closure of rooms to happen so suddenly. 'The clients don't need someone with them all the time,' I say. 'They can...'

'Anna! The pottery has to go; it's expensive to run. Materials, firing the kiln are...'

'But they love it.'

'I know, dear, but it's out of my hands.'

'What about my clients?'

'Some will be relocated to other rooms. Others will lose their service.'

I sit back into the chair. I was right. I'm going to be unemployed. 'So you're going to tell me I'm not needed.'

'No; we have a job for you.'

I look at her, mystified.

'We need someone to find our clients alternative places out in the community. We thought you'd be ideal for the job.'

I leave Margaret's office with a new job title. I am now Transitional Support Worker, though I've no idea where, or if, these alternative places exist.

I fasten my buttons; there's a chill in the air. I've been so caught up with thoughts of Sean I hadn't noticed summer fading; that leaves are on the ground, left to rot, like the countless letters and cards I've posted to Sean.

Bianco's lights send a welcome. I hurry across the road and into the bar. Vicky waves. I go over to her, saying, 'I'm sorry I'm so late.'

She pushes a long glass towards me. 'I thought you'd need something strong; the ice has melted but the gin won't have disappeared. What did she say?'

I take a sip of warm gin and tonic; then I tell her about my interview. 'It was good of her; she could have easily dismissed me.'

'She can be very supportive. The day after Craig left, I was so upset she took me into her office, went to the canteen and brought me back a cup of tea. I'm sure she would have let me have time off if I'd asked.'

I notice how well Vicky is looking. Her new hair style suits her, but it's not just that, or the little bit of make-up she's started to wear; her face is more relaxed, her eyes softer. 'You're looking good,' I tell her.

'I feel good. I'm beginning to see Craig for the two-timing piece of shit he is. I hear him and his new love aren't getting on but, do you know what, even if he came crawling back begging for forgiveness, I don't want him. I rather like being single. Liz helped a lot. She does this visualisation stuff. She taught me how to do it and it really does works. I certainly feel stronger, more able to cope. Anyway, what about you? How's Sean? Do you hear anything from him?'

'I hear disturbing news from the girls. They say he's unhappy. By all accounts, Diane nags and shouts at him; they think he's frightened of her. It's not as though he complains. They witness these things. They're very worried. They've tried to talk him into leaving and living with me. I asked them if he mentions my letters. They say he receives them. They think Diane throws them away.' I stop speaking and stare at the limp slice of lemon floating in my glass.

Vicky touches my hand. 'Why don't you give Liz a ring? Visualisation's not magic but it really helps.'

'I might.'

It's gone eight when we say goodbye. I hurry to the supermarket – I'm out of cat food; Lily will be frantic by now.

I spot Diane before she sees me. After making a quick retreat down an aisle, I look back at her.

The last time I saw her was in Ireland. She'd been sat in the Cinquecento, her face expressionless. The self-satisfaction she felt when Sean evicted me would have been invigorating. I can only imagine what happened next – the consoling, the agreement that he was much better off without me.

My first instinct was to stay out of her way but my need to speak with her is overwhelming. She almost jumps when she sees me.

'How's Sean?' I say.

Seconds tick by and I ask again. 'How is he?'

She almost spits the words at me. 'My time's taken up with trying to find something he can eat.' Dismissively, she turns back to the shelf. I stand watching her walk down the aisle, picking things up, putting them into her trolley, wishing I was the one who shops and cooks for him, who makes him comfortable, the one who cares.

'There's nothing magical about it,' says Liz. 'Most of us give ourselves negative thoughts. That's how visualisation works. The more we tell ourselves we aren't able or good enough to do this or that, the more convinced we become. But we can turn it round. Positive thoughts bring positive outcomes.' She points to the sofa. 'Lie down and I'll show you what I mean.'

Liz's voice is as soft as a lullaby. As I relax, the day centre and Diane become mere flecks in the sky.

'Picture Sean,' says Liz. 'Picture him in a room that you've made for him.'

I visualise him in the bedroom next to mine. I have furnished it, made it comfortable with lovely bedding and books he will want to read.

It's been a month since I saw Liz. I do feel better but nothing much has changed. The day centre whirls in a downward spiral. The clients worry they'll lose their friends and the rest of us wonder how long we'll have a job. I carry on dropping cards and letters into the post box, not expecting a reply, just wanting him to know I'm here for him.

When I answer the phone and hear Alice's voice, I'm unprepared for what she's telling me. It's when she repeats '...Is it okay, Mum? Dad wants to move in with you,' that I believe what I'm hearing.

CHAPTER 29

I use the cycle path most weekends – it's the quickest way to get to Alice's. When I reach the sign to Greenway Road, I always stop, look in the direction of Diane's house and think about Sean, wishing I could leave this path and go to him. He's been with her for six months; for six months I've been banished from his life, and now, the letter writing, the hunt for suitable cards has paid off.

Force of habit makes me stand still and look to where the signpost points. Sean is a five-minute walk away. He had been so far away from me. There are times when distance can't be measured by miles.

I spoke to Sean last night. He rang and told me the girls wanted him to move in with me. He said Diane wasn't coping, that she's been promoted and the longer hours were causing her stress.

Our conversation had been strained. The sentences clipped short. I kept my joy bubbling beneath the surface. When he told me Diane wanted to see me at her house this morning, I'd readily agreed. I want nothing to jeopardise his coming. Give neither of them an excuse to change their minds.

I reach Diane's house and press the doorbell. The rendering of "She'll be coming round the mountain" is so incongruous, so ridiculous to the occasion; I begin to wonder if any of this is real.

The door opens. Diane's face is cold enough to freeze a boiling kettle. I follow her into the lounge. Sean is sitting upright on a white leatherette sofa. I ask him how he is. He shrugs his shoulders and nods, as though one false word or move will tip his shrinking body onto the fluffy brown rug beneath his feet. Diane places herself behind him, rests her hands on his shoulders – Sean is so quiet I fear his personality has shrunk with his body. She looks at me with venom in her eyes when she says, 'We thought it would be best if he came later today.'

He probably won't remember today is our wedding anniversary. Wishfully, I hope fate will reunite us. Keeping delight from my voice, I say, 'Yes, that'll be fine. What time?'

'We'll drop off his things and pick up the keys around about five. I'll need a set for myself. We're having a meal out. When we're ready, I'll drive Sean to mine then he can get his car and drive to you. He shouldn't be late. I've an early start tomorrow.'

My expectation of an evening with Sean disappears. Putting aside my disappointment, I turn to him, saying, 'Lily will be pleased to see you.'

For the first time, he smiles. 'Do you mean I have to put up with her whining all day?'

'Yes and the grandchildren, they'll all be visiting.'

A look of impatience crosses Diane's face. 'He gets tired. He needs his rest.'

'Of course. Anyway, I must be off. I'll pop into B&Q and get those keys cut. I'll see you both later.'

Oscar is sitting in the hallway. His yellow eyes give a flash of anger. He dashes to the top of the stairs, sits staring down at me with his tail twitching.

Diane closes the lounge door, folds her arms and says, 'The reason he's coming to you is because work has become very stressful. I need to relax when I get home. After all, nursing your husband isn't my job.

'Sean told me about your promotion. Congratulations, and I quite understand why you feel the way you do. Anyway, I must get going; I've shopping to do.'

From the taxi to the door of my house takes two journeys. I put my purchases on the ground and I search for my key. Once I'm inside I unpack my goods. I take the new cordless phone from its box. Before I disconnect the old one, I check it for messages.

You have one new message.

'Anna! It's Eve. I need to talk to you.'

'Hello Eve.'

'Anna! I'm so glad you rang. It's just that... well, I'll come clean. After you left on Wednesday, David called in. He was asking about you. Wanted to know how you were. I told him you were okay but upset at not being able to see Sean. I told him how much you'd like to have him living with you. I wouldn't have told him if I'd known what he was going to do; honestly, I wouldn't. But this morning he rang and told me he'd got in touch with Diane. By all accounts, she's an ex-girlfriend of his. He told me he thinks he's convinced her that she should let Sean live with you. I hope this hasn't caused trouble. I'm so sorry if I've...'

'There's nothing to be sorry about. Sean's coming to live with me. Today, this evening, isn't it wonderful.'

CHAPTER 30

They're hardly here five minutes, just time enough to drop Sean's bags and fiddle into his room and pick up the keys. Lily rubs her body against Sean's leg. Diane hurries him past her saying, 'Leave the cat alone; I'm starving.'

I wait at the top of the stairs. When the door closes I listen for the engine to start. As soon as I hear the car turn at the end of the road I go into Sean's room.

His bags have been left on the floor, his old rucksack propped in a corner. The rucksack has been with him for as long as I can remember. I think back to when we moved into the bedsit, when I watched him unpack and felt the creases and crumples going straight to my heart.

On the bed is his fiddle case, its history written on the battered vinyl covering. I open it and look inside. The fiddle has led Sean a merry dance – merry music, merry drinking. If only I could have been merry and loved him for who he is.

I shut the case and open a drawstring bag. In it are bottles and packets of medication. Knowing how private he is about some things, I pull the drawstring, leave the bag as I found it.

I look around me. The bed linen and the rug are in the soft blues and greys he likes. Photographs of Kate, Alice and the children stand on an old chest of drawers that Sue gave me. On the bedside table is a reading lamp, a clock and an ashtray.

I leave the room and go onto the landing. The sound of fireworks draws me to my bedroom window. Next door's children are stood around a fire, their faces ruddy from the heat; sparklers making circles in the air – when Sean sees rockets flying through the night sky, will he remember what day it is today?

The phones rings. I run downstairs and pick it up. I carry it into the sitting room, listening to Chris saying, 'Anna! Kate told me Sean's moved in with you. We're so pleased; Diane wasn't coping. We all agreed he'd be better off with you. Can I have a word with him?'

'You've just missed him. They've – him and Diane – have gone out for a meal.' I haven't spoken to Chris since we met in the hospital. Feeling guilty, I try and explain. 'I'm sorry I haven't been in touch but...'

'Don't worry; I know how difficult it's been.'

'Yes, it has. Sean not wanting to see me was very upsetting. You had enough worries without me ringing and...'

'Look Anna, we're relieved he's with you. We would have had him here but he wanted to be near the girls. How is he?'

'He looks very tired. Other than a phone call a few days ago, I haven't had a chance to speak to him. They dropped off Sean's things, picked up the keys and left straightaway.'

With an edge of annoyance, she says, 'You'd have thought she'd be more concerned with settling him in than going out for meals.'

'I don't think they'll be late. After they've eaten she's taking him back to her house to collect the car and he'll be driving back here.'

'He's driving! He shouldn't be; he's on morphine. Wouldn't it be better if you got the car and fetched him?'

Part of me agrees with her, but Sean would hate to have his independence taken away. While he has his strength and is able, I'll let him decide what he can and can't do. 'Don't worry,' I say. 'It's a short drive and the road won't be busy. The girls are going to visit most days. Between us we'll keep a close eye on him.'

'I'm sure you will. We know he's in the best place.'

'I'm glad he's here. I'll do everything possible to make him comfortable. You know that you and Bill are welcome to stay whenever and as often as you want.'

I put the phone down. Minutes later Alice rings. Immediately after speaking to Alice, Kate is on the phone. They're disappointed Sean's not here. Both of them will call in to see him tomorrow.

It's gone nine. What did Diane mean when she said she didn't want to be late? How long does it take to eat a meal? Was Chris right when she said Sean shouldn't be driving? Has he had an accident?

I pick up a magazine and flip through the pages, put the magazine down, flick through the TV channels and turn it off. Sean and I never celebrated our wedding anniversary. No flowers, not even a card. When the children grew up and the fireworks stopped, our anniversary passed like any other day. But this time I wanted it to be different. I wanted an anniversary like no other.

The minutes drag by. It's gone ten-thirty when the familiar sound of the Cinquecento brings me to my feet. I stand in the passage, waiting to hear the key in the door.

I smile as brightly as my emotions will allow when I say, 'Did you have a nice time?'

'It was okay.' He moves towards the stairs, barely looking at me.

'Would you like a drink? I'll put the kettle on.'

'No thanks. I'll go on up to bed.'

He climbs the stairs and I say, 'Chris and the girls rang.'

'I'll ring them in the morning.'

He disappears on the landing and his door closes.

The wall that divides us does nothing to keep him from my mind. I listen for every sound. I wonder if he's as restless as I am. At two-thirty he leaves his room; the landing light shines through the crack of my door. The flush pulls, the light goes out, his door closes.

I turn the alarm off twenty minutes before its six-thirty wake-up call, relieved the night is over. Trying not to make a noise, I get dressed and go downstairs. Lily is nowhere to be seen. I fill her bowl and sit down to a solitary breakfast – there's a new dimension in this house, as light and delicate as a globe of dandelion seeds. One false move, a word, a step in the wrong direction, is likely to blow it away and be lost forever.

I clear the table, the clink of crockery cymbals to my ears, the gush from the tap a tsunami. I fear the slightest noise will start an avalanche.

I stand in front of his bedroom door; hesitate before giving a light tap. I wait a minute then gently turn the handle.

Lily is curled up on his bed; she opens one eye and gives me a brief stare. Sean's head is beneath the duvet.

'Sean,' I whisper, then slightly louder, 'Sean.'

His head appears above the duvet and he demands, 'What?'

'I'm going to work; is there anything I can get you?'

'No thanks.'

'Tea, coffee, water?'

'No, I don't want anything.'

'Would you like me to bring up the phone? Chris is going to ring. The girls will want to let you know when they're coming.'

'I'll get it myself.'

'I've filled Lily's bowl. There's plenty of food in the fridge. Help yourself when you're...'

He pushes the duvet away, sits up with eyes alight with anger. 'For fuck's sake, leave me alone; I'll see to myself when I'm ready.'

Work has become a refuge. The little room next to reception – now the Transitional Support Worker's office – holds another world. When I close its door, my own worries are replaced with the traumas and sufferings of others. The phone rings constantly with relatives and clients desperate and pleading to keep the day centre open. I'm about to dial a community centre that runs luncheon clubs when the door opens and Vicky walks in. 'How did you get on?' she asks. 'Did you see Sean?'

I put the phone down and swivel my chair around to face her. 'Yes, he moved in last night.'

'That's wonderful news.' She sits on the chair reserved for clients and says, 'What a relief. How is he?'

'We hardly spoke. He dropped his things off and he and Diane went out for a meal.'

'How's he look?'

'When was the last time you saw him? It must have been before we moved to Ireland. You'll be shocked. He certainly looks better than when I saw him in hospital, but he's very thin; skin and bones really.' I stop speaking, remembering how he'd reacted this morning. 'But the old Sean's still there, there's still a lively tune left in the old fiddle.' The phone rings. I turn to answer it, saying, 'I'm sorry, I must get this.'

She stands up. 'I'm so pleased for you, Anna. I'll see you lunch time.'

I've had a niggling feeling that Diane would be in the house. Seeing her car parked in the street confirmed it. She appears on the stairs, looks down at me with one hand on the banister, the other on her hip, saying, 'I caught him smoking.'

I unbutton my coat. 'Did you?'

'Yes. He was smoking. Did you buy him cigarettes?'

'No.'

'Then where did he get them from?'

'Perhaps he bought them when he was out with you.'

I turn my back to her and hang my coat on the hook.

'How did the ashtray get into his room?'

I turn to face her. 'I put it there. He smokes. He's going to need it.'

'You're encouraging him. It's bad for him. You should be stopping him.'

'He's a grown man. He'll decide whether he smokes or not.'

She follows me into the kitchen, shouting, 'He has cancer. He's very ill. He shouldn't be smoking.'

I close the kitchen door. 'Diane, he's dying. Not smoking won't save him. And I'd rather you didn't shout.'

She looks at me with narrowed eyes. 'You never cared about him, did you. What if he sets the bed on fire; he'll burn to death; the house could go up in flames.'

I pick up the kettle. 'I'm insured. I'll look for the quickest exit.' I turn on the tap and fill the kettle. When I look round Diane is gone.

I hear her raised voice, a few minutes later her step treading down the stairs. The front door opens and slams.

Sean walks into the kitchen. 'Have you two been arguing?

I put another mug next to mine. 'She doesn't approve of you smoking.'

'She's allergic to cigarette smoke. When I was with her I smoked outside.'

I fill the mugs and take them to the table. We sit opposite each other. He puts a cigarette to his mouth and takes a drag. I'm about to ask if the girls came when he says, 'I've told Diane, I've told Dad and Chris, I've told the girls that I own half this house. I've as much right to be here as you have.'

'I know,' I say, putting my hand out to touch his.

He moves his hand away. 'I can't forgive what you did, but I need a place to live. Diane was finding it difficult. After chemo I feel bloody awful. Some days I haven't energy for anything. I need someone around.'

I want to tell him I can't forgive myself. Words fail me and for a few moments we sit in silence.

'Tell me when you're hungry,' I say. 'I bought ham the way you like it, straight off the bone, and there's eggs.'

He stands up. 'Perhaps later. I'm going to play a few tunes.'

I stay sat at the table, listening to his music, watching his tea go cold, realising my wish for a reunion was just a foolish dream.

CHAPTER 31

Liz and I are sat on Liz's futon. 'It's been over three weeks since he's been with me,' I tell her. 'Believe me, I'm glad he came; I wouldn't want it any other way, but I didn't bank on Diane coming so often. She calls in every evening. She doesn't give a time. It could be on her way home from work. Or later, after she's eaten, so I can never settle down to anything. But it's weekends I find the most difficult. I've become used to slopping around in my dressing gown – you know what I mean: having a late breakfast in front of the TV, doing a bit of shopping, inviting you and the girls round for an evening meal. But all that's had to stop. I can't do anything with her there. I don't regret Sean coming, not at all, but I wish it was just the two of us. I must admit it's getting me down; if only she could be more pleasant. She interferes, tutting over everything, re-washing mugs after I've washed them, complaining that the hand towel in the bathroom needs changing. Last Saturday I popped out to do a bit of shopping; when I got back she proudly showed me a duster. She held it out, pointing to a smear of dirt. "It's from your TV screen," she said with glee in her eyes. I took it from her, smiled and said, "Thanks," while all the time wanting to slap the enjoyment right off her stupid face. In the afternoon I went into the garden, mainly to get away from her. I was admiring the holly bush with its bright red berries, when up she marches and tells me I should get rid of it. She said the berries might be poisonous and what if the children ate them. I was outraged. I said to her, "Diane, they're not poisonous: birds eat them. People take them into their house for decoration. Children need to learn what they can and can't do. We need to show them what the hazards are. How is pulling out my holly bush going to help? There's millions of holly bushes out there and probably hundreds of poisonous plants!" She didn't say anything, just pursed her mean little mouth and went inside.'

I look at Liz, expecting her to agree with me that Diane is a bitch. But she raises an eyebrow, gives me a shrewd look and says, 'You need to get away for a few days. Why don't you come here?'

'That's good of you, and if things get too difficult I will. My sister rang the other evening and invited me to stay with them. I haven't seen her for ages... but... if I go... I know this sounds as though I'm jealous but... but if I do, Diane will stay the night. She won't take Sean to her house. Oh no, she'll want to show me how much control she has. Sean's bed is single so they'll sleep in mine. Both of them in my bed! I don't know if I can bear that.'

'Anna!' I know from Liz's tone of voice what's coming. 'You're jealous. You're seething... it's eating you up. For Christ's sake, what if they do sleep in your bed. If he's as ill as you say, they're hardly going to be humping all night and, honestly, what if they are. It'll probably do him the world of good. Leave them alone. Let them have a weekend together. She might be a lot nicer when you get back.'

Her words shake me. Tears roll down my face. She puts her arm around me, saying, 'I understand how difficult it must be, but Sean's the one who's suffering. Surely he has enough on his plate without two women arguing over him.' She takes my hand. 'How is he? How are you getting on together?'

'We're okay. He's very quiet, keeps his distance. It's as though he's put a barrier between us. We had a nice time a few evenings ago. Kate came and brought her flute. She and Sean played a few tunes together. We shared a bottle of wine. Sean only had one glass. Yes, we had a very nice evening. For once, Diane wasn't there.'

'Do you still visualise?'

I nod.

'Do you find it helpful?'

'Yes, very.'

'Good. Listen, when you get home, ring Jenny. A few days of sisterly love is what you need.'

Sean and Diane are watching television together, both of them engrossed in some sort of quiz show – "Family Fortunes" or something like that. I stand in the doorway, looking at them. Their eyes are glued to the screen. 'Hi,' I say. The quick glance they give me hardly acknowledges I'm here.

I don't understand it. Sean was never interested in this sort of entertainment. He would prefer to watch a documentary. Or better still, to turn off the television and listen to music.

Seeing Sean and Diane sat side by side, a picture of harmonious bliss, makes me envious. Forcing myself to smile, I say, 'I'm going to stay with my sister for the weekend.' – I knew that would make them look at me. I muster up the brightest smile I can find. 'Sorry, I'm disturbing you. I'll let you get on watching your programme.'

I've put clean bedding on my bed. A beef casserole is on the kitchen worktop, ready to go into the oven. I've made the casserole the way Sean likes it – plenty of meat flavoured with spices and herbs. As a little extra, I put in four cloves of garlic. I overheard Diane telling Sean she doesn't eat garlic; it gives her diarrhoea.

I push my way onto the Southampton train, just managing to grab an aisle seat. Feeling lucky I'm not amongst those standing, I sit back, ready to enjoy some time to myself.

Work has become quite eventful. Most of my time is taken up with relatives and social workers but one of the relatives, a man called Steve, has asked me to become involved with a group of people who are fighting to keep the day centre open. He told me they've made contact with a solicitor who, being sympathetic to our cause, has offered her services free of charge. She needs to look at clients' records, of course, and, as a transitional support worker, I have access to them.

Almost a year has passed since Jenny and I were saying goodbye on the station platform in Southampton. Back then, I would never have guessed, not in a million years, that on that very same day I'd be saying goodbye to David.

I see the truth more clearly now. David was never interested in a serious relationship; that was what I'd wanted. David's not a bad person; he obviously cares about Sean. Without him, Sean might still be with Diane.

Liz was right; I needed to get away and spend time with Jenny. She listened to my rants and complaints, made me examine why I'd wanted Sean to stay with me and who I was doing it for. 'Why, Sean of course,' I repeated, over and over again, until l understood and saw the truth.

The hours flip by. Before I know it, Jenny and I are on the platform and the train's arriving. 'Don't forget I'm here for you,' she says. And I try to remember when we changed roles, when I became the little sister, the needy one.

I wanted the journey to last forever, but all too soon I'm leaving the station and stepping onto the number 21 bus.

Diane's car is nowhere in sight. I go into the house; her coat's not hanging in the hall. Sean leaves the sitting-room, stands in the doorway and asks, 'Did you have a good weekend?'

'Yes, thanks. What about you?'

'It was alright.'

He follows me into the kitchen, and I ask, 'What about Diane? Is she okay?'

'Yes. She left a few minutes ago.'

'Do you want a drink?'

'No thanks.'

I have a feeling he wants to tell me something.

'We were talking about Christmas,' he says. 'She wants me to spend it with her.'

My resolve to be understanding begins to crumble. 'But... the girls... they'll be so disappointed... Don't you want to watch the children open their presents?'

'I asked her if she'd like to go to Alice's or Kate's, or if they could go to her house. She said she wants it to be just the two of us. She said families make her feel sad. She has no one; I can't let her down. She's been good to me. Without her, I don't know what I'd have done.'

I understand what he is telling me. I divided this family. I've no one to blame but myself.

CHAPTER 32

I lie in bed, listening for the smallest noise – the pad of the cat, the drop of a pin, a sigh. I open my eyes to a grey morning and stare up at the ceiling, lost in the blankness, the nothingness, the flat whiteness, wanting nothing more than to stay in the uneventfulness of it.

A creak from Sean's room forces me to sit up, drag my feet from the weight of the covers and sit on the edge of the bed, listening, wishing I could have buried my head under the duvet, stayed hidden until Christmas had passed.

The house is quiet. Even on workdays, when I'm hurrying to leave and Lily is crying incessantly for her breakfast, there is a hush. This morning it is tenfold, hangs in the air as hard as ice, freezing any thoughts that Christmas might be the season of love and joy.

I will myself to stand, put on my slippers and dressing gown. I hesitate for a moment at his door. There are no words; nothing I can I say or do will drop his defence, lift this exclusion. The door, his room have become a fortress.

In the sitting room, displayed in a silver pot, are two stems of hogweed. I picked them from the edge of the cycle path, brought them home and sprayed them red and gold. Silver baubles hang from the spindly stalks, catching the light from the window. I might as well have put a crown on a beggar, a diamond ring on a work-worn nail bitten hand; it doesn't change things. The weed is still a weed. The three brightly wrapped parcels on the coffee table, the dozen or so cards lining the shelf haven't brought any cheer. It takes more than a few trinkets to encourage the spirit of goodwill to enter this house.

The small parcel is from Blodwyn to me. I unwrap it and find a tiny box. Inside the box is a silver angel. A note says,

Dear babe, an angel for your pocket. I'm here when you need me, Love Blod x.

I've become so neglectful of my friends; I don't deserve them. Other than work, I spend my time in this house. Trying to be unobtrusive; waiting in the wings to do Sean's bidding.

The two remaining parcels are from Chris and Bill. The shape and softness of them suggest they are jumpers. They left the parcels here a week ago. I think they would have stayed for Christmas if Sean hadn't been going to Diane's. I'm hoping Sean and I will open our parcels together. I would like to share one little Christmas ceremony before Diane takes him away.

I go to the shelf, single out two cards from the others. One of the cards has a picture of baby Jesus in his mother's arms. On the other, three Kings kneel beside a crib. The cards are from Bridie and Mary and Tom.

I wrote to them four weeks ago, apologising for not being in touch. I didn't go into details. I didn't tell them about David. I told them Sean has cancer and is now living with me. Within a fortnight their replies dropped through my door. I showed the letters to Sean; he told me to get rid of them, that Diane would be upset if she read them. I couldn't throw them away so I've hidden them in my dressing table drawer. I don't care if she does find them, or if Bridie and Mary's words upset her – *We are praying for Sean's recovery. Thank God you and Sean are together again, and we'll see you both very soon.*

I hear Sean's door open, Lily's pad on the stairs. I put the cards back onto the shelf. Lily follows me into the kitchen. I fill her bowl, make tea for Sean and carry it up to him.

Sean is getting back into bed. I put the drink onto his bedside table, asking, 'What time's Diane collecting you?' Driving is one more thing he's unable to do. He looks at the clock. 'Some time later this morning.'

'Would you like some breakfast?' I stop at the doorway, waiting for his reply.

He shakes his head. 'Diane's cooking lunch. I'd better not.'

'Well, let me know if there's anything you want. I'm going to have a bite to eat then I'm getting ready to go out. Call me if you need anything.'

It's gone eleven when Sean comes into the kitchen. I'm wearing a new blue velvet shirt, my hair clipped back with a silver slide. I've put on mascara and a little lipstick. The parcels from Chris and Bill are on the table in front of me. Next to them is a pair of scissors to cut the gold twine.

'You look nice,' I say, noting his fresh shave and the green jumper that matches the colour of his eyes. He looks at the parcels. I remind him, 'They're from Chris and your Dad. I thought we'd open them together.' Seeing the frown on his face, I instantly say, 'Don't worry, I haven't bought you anything. We agreed not to?' I wait for him to pick up his parcel, whilst saying, 'The girls' and the children's presents from us are packed in my bag. I spoke to Jenny yesterday and thanked her for the book tokens.'

The parcels wait on the table. I pick up his and pass it to him.

'Another sweater,' he says. 'I won't open it now. I'll take it to Diane's. She'll be here soon. I'll wait in the sitting room.'

Twenty minutes go by before the front door opens and closes. There was no goodbye. I pick up my parcel and open it. The jumper is bright red with fluffy toggles and embroidered snowflakes. I don't know why I keep looking at it. It's nothing I would want to wear, so jolly it makes me want to cry.

They won't let me do a thing. Alice and Kate are nattering in the kitchen, opening the oven to the smell of roast turkey.

Saucepans send sprout and carrot steam through the open kitchen window. I go into the lounge, gasp with surprise at Stella and Ella's pile of toys.

Ella performs a trick from her box of magic while I nurse Stella's latest baby doll. 'That's fantastic, Ella. Would you like me to put your baby in her pram, Stella?'

Sam and Adam are looking under the bonnet of the car. Alice shouts from the front door, 'Adam, Sam, you'd better finish that now. Come in and wash your hands. We'll be eating in about fifteen minutes.'

'Let's raise a glass to Dad,' says Alice.

'I wish he was with us,' says Kate.

We nod in agreement and a sprinkle of sadness falls across the table.

'Crackers!' call the children, waving them in the air.

'Who's going to pull one with me?' asks Adam.

'I will,' they shout, wiping sadness away.

Alice takes my plate. 'Weren't you hungry?' she asks.

I shake my head – it's not just my appetite that's left me. 'I'm sorry,' I say. 'I don't feel that special, just a small amount of pudding.'

She puts a portion in front of me and I ask, 'What time are Adam's parents coming?'

Twenty minutes later, Elaine and Bob enter the house, their arms full of parcels, their smiles as bright as painted banners.

'Anna!' says Elaine. 'It's been ages since we saw you. When was it? I know: the christening. How long ago was that? Let's see, it must be all of sixteen months.' She sits next to me, saying, 'So much has happened to you. I've heard all about it. Adam and Alice tell me everything. There're no secrets in our family. How's Sean? It must be terrible for you knowing he has a girlfriend.' She looks at Bob. 'I don't know what I'd do if Bob was unfaithful.' Lowering her voice, she whispers, 'I'm sure Sean wouldn't be with her if you hadn't left him for... what was his name?'

'Do you want a drink, Elaine?' asks Alice, coming to the rescue.

'Yes please, darling. Brandy and Babycham if you have it.'

'We bought it specially for you. What about you, Mum?'

'Not for me. I'm driving. If you don't mind, I think I'll go soon. I don't feel too good.'

'Let me give you your present,' says Elaine.

'Would you like me to drive you home?' asks Alice. 'You can get the car tomorrow.'

I thank Elaine for her present, turn to Alice, saying, 'I'm fine to drive. I'll be home in five minutes.'

I would've liked a few minutes sat quietly in the car on my own. But Alice and Kate's anxious faces are watching me from the door. I give them a final wave and drive away.

The red jumper is where I'd left it, lying like a pool of blood across the table. In the sitting room the silver and red baubles shout, "See! We couldn't help you. It was all rather pathetic, the new blouse, the hair-do. You've cooked your goose, Anna. You got exactly what you deserve."

I'm about to throw the baubles onto the floor when I hear Diane's car pull up outside the house.

Sean walks into the room. 'You're early,' I say.

He gives a weary nod and sits on the sofa.

'I'll put the heating on. There might be something on tele.'

For a moment he doesn't answer, then he lifts his head, looks me in the eye, saying, 'You broke my heart, Anna. It was terrible. You gave me no warning. I couldn't understand what was happening. What I'd done, until I heard it was

David. You left me for David. How could you? Did you hate me that much?'

I soak up his words, wanting to take his pain, make him whole. I stumble out of the room. My legs feel like jelly. I grab the newel post and...

Sean's voice is asking, 'Are you alright?'

He helps me up and I say, 'I felt unwell all afternoon.'

He follows me to my room, pulls the duvet back. 'Have a rest,' he says. 'I'll see how you are later.'

I don't know how long I've been crying and sleeping. How many hours had passed when I hear him say, 'Are you feeling better?'

I take his hand. A hand I don't recognise. A hand that is so soft I feel it must belong to someone else. 'Will you come into bed with me?' I ask.

He gets in beside me, puts his arm around me and I fall into a deep sleep. The movement of him leaving wakes me. I hear the door open and close. I touch where he had been lying, taking comfort from the small patch of warmth left behind.

CHAPTER 33

I'm hurrying through the park, trying to get to work on time, when my phone rings. I slow down, grab it from my pocket. A man's voice says, 'Anna, it's Steve. Will you be in the office today? We need a photocopy of Maud Griffin's file. Can you get one done this morning?' Maud is another of our clients, desperately worried she's about to be abandoned and forgotten when the day centre closes.

'I'm on my way to work now. I can get you a copy by this afternoon.'

'That'll be great. I don't know how the bastards can live with themselves; so many depend on the centre, particularly people like Maud with no family. They might as well lock them in a cell and condemn them to solitary confinement.'

'I agree. I wish I could do more, but Sean... well, what time I have I want to spend with him.'

'Of course, he comes first. Having you give us copies of the files is fantastic. The solicitor can't do anything without them.'

'I'm outside the centre now. Before I go in, tell me what's happening.'

'We're taking a group to the city centre. A coach company has offered to ferry us all down there. Our clients are going to stop the traffic. They'll keep crossing the road, back and forth; some of them in wheelchairs, others with Zimmer frames, until the road's gridlocked. It's the only way. We've got to make an impact,'

'Brilliant. I must go. See you later.'

Finding and photocopying Maud's file is not a problem. Trying to find people like Maud an alternative to the day centre is. Lunch Clubs, that's the answer, or so I'm told by those who think they know best. Yes, there are Lunch Clubs in church halls and community centres throughout the city. But let the people who sit in the Council House making decisions go looking for them. The same problems arise time and time again. However I put it, I'm always asked, 'Can they make their own way?'

My answer is always the same. 'They're physically disabled... They have dementia... They have no family... They can't afford a taxi.' For those who can make their own way, I'm told, 'I can put them on the waiting list for the waiting list.'

It's so frustrating, which is why it's empowering when Steve comes into the office and I hand him Maud's file. 'Have you had any luck finding my dad a place?' he asks.

With a voice loud enough to be heard in reception, I say, 'Sorry Steve, nothing's turned up yet. You'll have to make your complaints directly to Social Services.'

My phone rings. 'Excuse me,' I say, 'I must see who this is.' I go to my coat and fish for my phone. It's Sean... 'Hello,' I say, leaving the room. 'Sean, are you all right?' I go through reception. 'What's happened?' I go outside. 'Sean, tell me. What's the matter?'

I hear his sobs when he says, 'They've stopped my chemo. It's not working. There's nothing more they can do for me.'

'I'm coming home. I'll be with you as soon as I can.'

I rush back into the building, through reception and into my office. 'I'm going home,' I tell Steve. 'I need to be with Sean.'

I pick up my bag and coat and hurry to Margaret's office. Giving the door a sharp tap, I go inside, saying, 'I've had a call from Sean. He needs me. I'm going home.'

I don't wait for a reply, don't stop to say goodbye, or sign out.

Steve is sitting in his car. He opens the door. 'Get in. Where do you live?'

I enter the house, call Sean's name, glance in the sitting room, then go to the kitchen. He is sat at the table; Lily is on his lap. His eyes speak volumes – the delicate lace of fine red veins, irises like freshly washed algae show the depth of his pain. I sit next to him, lay my hand on his shoulder, urging him to understand his pain is mine.

'Did Kate stay long?' I whisper.

'About an hour. She had to be in work at two.' Suddenly he bangs his fist onto the table. Lily jumps to the floor. 'I'm so fucking angry,' he says. 'I wouldn't have had fucking chemo if I'd known. God, it made me ill. All that for nothing.'

He rests his elbows on the table. Holding his head in his hands, he stares at the chequered cloth.

I search my mind for an answer. 'There must be something we can do,' I say. 'What about going private? We own three houses. We can sell one. We can sell them all,' I pronounce, clutching at straws, screaming at the voice inside my head to shut up. I won't let him die. I won't, I won't.

'Money won't help,' he says. 'There's nothing anybody can do.'

A sound of uncontrollable sobs, as though a heart is breaking, comes from nowhere. Sean is stroking my hair, turning my face to his, wiping away my tears with his fingers.

I hear the front door open and close, Diane's heavy step walking towards the kitchen. 'Where's Sean?' she demands, expecting to see him sitting at the table.

'He's in bed. He was asleep when I looked in a few minutes ago.'

She turns back to the hall. 'I'll go up.'

'He's tired,' I say following her. 'Those trips to the hospital tire him. Perhaps it'll be better if you wait until tomorrow.'

She stops on the stair and looks down at me. 'Don't tell me what I can and can't do. It's not for you to decide if I see him or not.'

I doubt if she'll stay long. Since he's become so frail she's in and out in minutes. His waking hours are shrinking. He can't manage half an hour of television without falling asleep. Reading makes him tired. She's hardly had time to walk into his room and out again when I hear her descending the stairs, the front door closing behind her.

I look at the clock, wondering if Sean will be awake for seven. Seven o'clock has become the highlight of our day, the time when Kate and I – if her shift allows – join Sean for a roll-up and a glass of wine. Sometimes we sit in the lounge but, more often than not, it's in his room. Sean propped up in bed with pillows. Kate and I sat at his bedside.

One evening Kate announced, 'These are the best parties I've ever been to.' Sean looked at her, smiled and said, 'Poor girl, you must have been to some bloody awful parties,' and then we were laughing.

I carry a bottle of Beaujolais to his room. He's asleep. I dread the party and laughter coming to an end.

I walk from work, through the park, following the river. Sometimes in summer the river is hardly more than a stream. We're now in February and after a week of heavy rain the river roars with energy. Chris and Bill have been staying with us so I've been able to take my time, enjoying the walk home. But they went yesterday and I can't help panicking at the thought of Sean being on his own. The park does nothing to brighten my mood. The sky is pewter grey, the air damp, the trees bare. As I follow the curve of the river, a shaft of light falls from a crack in the cloud, a streak of blue darts towards the bank.

Someone once told me that kingfishers are messengers of the gods; this one is telling me to hurry home, and I do.

I walk into the sitting-room. He looks terrible. He opens his eyes. Tries to lift himself up from the sofa. 'I feel dreadful,' he says.

'Why aren't you in bed?' I ask.

'The doctor came. I wanted to be up and dressed. He was so kind. He made me a cup of tea.'

'Have you seen Diane?'

'I heard a knock but didn't have the energy to answer.'

'What about her key? Has she lost it again?'

He shakes his head.

'Sean,' I say, taking his hand. 'This won't happen again. I'll tell them tomorrow. They'll have to find someone else to do the job. I want to be with you.'

CHAPTER 34

I hadn't expected Margaret to be so understanding. After all, I didn't give her a moment's notice. I told her I was leaving without considering who might take my job. Didn't give a thought to the clients I'm trying to help. The only person in my head was Sean. Everything I do is for him. So I was stunned when she said, 'My dear, of course you should be with your husband. I've been thinking, you can do this job just as well from home as you can from here. We'll reimburse you for phone calls. You'll need to look at files and keep us updated, but you don't live that far away, do you?'

My mouth opened with surprise. For a moment I was speechless. 'So, I've still got my job?' I said.

'Yes,' she said, and I felt as though a gift had landed on my lap. To be with Sean and keep my job was more than I would have dared wish for.

Sean and I have become, how shall I say, comfortable together. We wear each other like a favourite item of clothes. Despite the frayed edges, the worn patches, I want to hold on tight, frightened to lose these last precious moments with him. The trouble is my favourite garment is beyond repair, disappearing before my eyes; soon it will disintegrate.

The days fly by like clouds. I want to grab them. Hold on to morning before the day darkens and disappears into yesterday. Every moment I spend with him is precious. Caring for him, being with him, is all I want.

Within a week of working from home, we've settled into a routine. At eight-fifteen I clear away my breakfast bowl and mug and turn the kitchen table into a desk.

Before I start work, I peep into Sean's room. Today he is in a deep sleep, Lily a small lump beneath the bedclothes. I go back to the kitchen table and put pen to paper. The phone hardly stops ringing. Whenever there's a moment between talking to clients, relatives, or social workers, I hurry to Sean's room. More often than not he is asleep.

I stop work at twelve, switch the phone to answer, and make a drink. I go up to Sean's room and find him asleep. I put the drink onto the bedside table and pat his shoulder. Lily crawls from under the covers, gives me a look of disdain, before jumping to the floor and leaving the room. Sean opens his eyes. 'I'm nipping down for the paper,' I tell him.

Looking through the local paper for any news to do with the day centre has become one of the focuses of our day. When I get back, he is sitting up in bed. He looks quite bright; like me, he enjoys this mid-day hour.

'Nothing on the front page,' I say, putting the paper onto the bed. I pull a chair to his bedside and together we look through the pages.

'Ha, here,' he says, pointing to a few paragraphs on page five. Reading aloud, he says, '*Steve Williams, spokesperson for Save Meadow View Day Centre, told our reporter, "We won't be beaten. We'll chain ourselves to the railings if we have to."*'

He passes the page to me and I give it a quick scan. 'Well, they won't,' I say, putting the page back onto the bed. 'Most of our clients are too old and infirm to be chaining themselves to railings. They're running out of ideas but what else can they do? They've stopped traffic. They've stormed the Labour Party headquarters. The public are getting bored. They need something else to draw attention. Where do you think they should go from here?'

'Tug at their heart strings,' is his quick reply. 'Get the paper to write some of their personal stories. You know the sort of thing – poor young girl in a wheelchair; parents can't cope so she's living in sheltered accommodation. The only time she meets her friends is at the day centre. Get a few photos; though, make sure she's pretty. That'll get them weeping. I think there's too much emphasis on the protest and not enough on the people losing the service.'

'You're right. That's a brilliant idea. I was planning to ring Steve today. I'll tell him what you said.'

'I don't know why one of your lot didn't think about it themselves,' he says with a smile.

At about twelve-thirty, Sean comes downstairs wearing his dressing gown and we have lunch together. The rest of the afternoon he spends on the sofa, reading or listening to music. I carry on working until about 3.00 p.m. If Alice calls in, I'll put the phone down and go out and do a bit of shopping, take in a prescription to the chemist. She doesn't stay long; the children tire him. A shadow falls when Diane arrives at five – Sean's in bed by then so I don't see much of her – but I still heave a sigh of relief when, half an hour later, her footsteps come down the stairs and the door closes behind her.

Kate visits when she can. She always brings her flute but leaves it in her bag. It's unspoken, but I think she doesn't want to remind Sean of the times they've played music together. Those days are gone; his fiddle will sleep until another master plucks its strings.

At six in the evening, I go to his room and roll us both a cigarette. He still enjoys smoking, but the glass of wine is often left on the bedside table, untouched. By seven, his eyes start to close. I take the cigarette from his fingers, sit for a while by his side then leave him to sleep.

I feel we are floating in a bubble, the two of us pushed along by the gentlest of breeze. I know this tranquil journey is coming to an end, that the bubble is about to burst and a thousand tears are ready to fall.

Today is Thursday. On Thursdays we have a different routine. Sean is up, dressed and bathed by nine. He does this without my assistance – as always, he's fiercely independent. Why he has to be dressed and looking as though he's about to go out when the doctor visits is a question I can't answer. I hear the knock on the door. I don't get up. It won't be Alice. She knows not to come on a Thursday.

I put down my pen, switch the phone to answer, and listen. Sean and the doctor are talking in the hallway. They go into the sitting room and the door closes.

Sean won't like what I'm about to do. He would prefer me not to be with him when the doctor is here. I give a light tap on the door then open it. Sean frowns when he sees me. Dr Esler looks at me questioningly. 'Anna Curtin,' I say, holding out my hand, 'Sean's wife.'

Esler stands up, 'Oh, I didn't realise you were home. I thought you were at work.'

'Not now,' I say, sitting next to Sean. 'I work from home.'

'Good,' says Esler, sitting back down. 'I'm glad to hear it. In fact, I'm glad you're here. I want to discuss with Sean whether or not he will want to go into a hospice.'

I feel Sean stiffen beside me. I don't have to look at him to know what expression is on his face. I keep my eyes focused on Esler. Esler looks at Sean, asking, 'Do you want me to book you a room in a hospice?'

Sean clears his throat before saying, 'No.'

'Would you like to think about it?'

'I don't want to go into a hospice. I prefer to be at home.'

'What about you, Mrs Curtin? Are you able to manage? If Sean...'

Before he can say any more, I interrupt. 'It's up to Sean. What he wants is what I want.'

'What about a nurse? The Macmillan's do a...'

I hold up my hand. 'No, Sean doesn't want or need a nurse. We can manage perfectly well without help.'

I like Esler. He's not my doctor, but I feel he's there for both of us. There's a burning question I need to ask, however painful the answer might be. I can't ring from home. I don't want Sean to hear what I have to say. After mulling it over all weekend, I decide to go to the day centre and ring the surgery from there.

'I won't be here in the morning,' I say, as I roll Sean his night-time cigarette. 'I've got to go to the day centre. I need to deliver a few files and show them the telephone bill. I won't be long. I'll take the car.'

I time my call for the end of morning surgery. 'My husband's a patient of Dr Esler,' I tell the receptionist. 'I need to talk to him... Yes, it's urgent... It's Sean Curtin's wife. We met when you visited on Thursday. I want to know what the prognosis is?'

'Weeks,' he says in a gentle voice.

'Weeks,' I whisper. 'How many. How many weeks?'

'Two, three, it won't be long.'

I put down the phone – numbers flip through my mind like those on a calendar.

I stop on my way home and tell Alice the news. Trying not to let her tears start mine, I take her arms from mine, saying, 'I must go; Dad will wonder where I am. Let Kate know,' I say, before hurrying away.

It's as though the doctor's prediction has started the ball rolling. Today Sean is not interested in the paper. Even when I show him the front-page picture of Lucy, a young girl with spina bifida and her boyfriend Michael who has cerebral palsy – if the centre closes they may never see each other again.

Sean doesn't want to leave his bed. He refuses lunch. All he wants to do is sleep. The bottle of morphine on Sean's bedside table is nearly empty – he takes more than the prescribed dose. I ring Alice and tell her I need to take a prescription into the chemist. 'I can't leave him,' I say, 'he's very poorly.'

'I'll be round in ten minutes.'

I put on my coat and wait at the window. Soon Stella is trotting up the path. Her bright eyes and rosy cheeks bring a flash of colour to the darkness stretching in front of me.

'Shh,' I say as she runs into the house. 'Go into the sitting room with Mummy; the big box of toys is there.'

'Don't rush,' says Alice. 'My neighbour's collecting Ella from school.' I open the door ready to leave. Stop when she says, 'I saw Diane. She was driving past as we were leaving. She pulled up. I told her what the doctor said.'

'You what?'

'I told her... Why? What's the matter?'

'You shouldn't have.'

'Why?'

'Because she won't like it. She'd want to be the first to know.'

'That's silly. She...'

'Alice, I know what she's like. She'll be furious. She'll be round here shouting, making a fuss. I don't want Sean being disturbed.'

Desperate to speak to Diane, I quickly leave the house. When I'm out of earshot, I take the phone from my bag and call Diane's number. I leave a message. 'Alice told me she spoke to you. I planned to tell you myself, but I've been busy. I'm sorry.' – I'll crawl to her if I have to. I want nothing upsetting the peace in my house.

Have you ever felt the sky tumbling on top of you, black cloud on black cloud, until there's nothing but darkness, while, all the time, the evil magician brings yet another joke from his box of tricks.

I look at the slip of paper in the chemist assistant's hand. 'I told you,' she says, 'I can't take this prescription; the doctor hasn't signed it.'

I snatch it from her. 'What do you mean?'

'There's no signature, he's forgotten to sign it.'

I slam the prescription down onto the counter. Trying to make her dull face understand, I shout, 'You know who I am. I give you this prescription every week.'

'We can't take it without a signature.'

She calls for the chemist – an elderly man wearing half-moon glasses. Like wooden dolls, they stare at me.

'My husband needs his medication!' I scream. 'I can't go home without it.'

'You'll have to take it back to the surgery,' says the chemist. 'Get the doctor to sign it.'

'It's one-thirty. The fucking surgery will be closed!'

'I'd rather you didn't swear,' says the chemist as he and his assistant move closer together.

Tears roll down my face. I snatch the prescription. Customers part as I push my way through the shop. I sit in the car, waiting for my heart to slow down.

'Don't worry,' says Alice, 'Adam or I will take it to the surgery this evening. There's a late night chemist in town. One of us will bring it straight to you.'

Relieved, I go up Sean's room. His bed is empty. I look in the bathroom. Panicking, I run downstairs, calling, 'Where is he?'

Alice looks up from her game with Stella. 'In the garden.'

I go outside, and there he is, a phantom of himself, wearing his old grey dressing gown while sweeping the garden path. I open the back door and call, 'I wondered where you were.'

He looks up at me, saying, 'This path's a mess.'

I was hoping Alice and Stella would still be with me. I know it's cowardly, but I thought them being here might curb Diane's temper. They left an hour ago, I've been on tenterhooks ever since.

Sean is up in bed, listening to music. I'm praying he won't hear Diane screaming at me like a Sergeant Major.

I've placed myself by the window, ready for action. When I see Diane at the gate, I go to the hallway and stand at the door. I hear the key go into the latch. The door opens. She looks at me with a face red with fury, saying, 'I should have been the first to know.' She tries to push past me. 'Let me in,' she shouts. Holding tightly to door frame, I stand firm.

'Not until you calm down. I don't want Sean to hear us arguing. We mustn't upset him. He's the important one.'

'We're all important.'

'Not in this house,' I say, standing aside. 'Sean's the important one here.'

She doesn't stay much longer than ten minutes. When she leaves, I go to Sean's room and he asks, 'Were you two arguing?'

'She had a little moan about the lack of parking in the street, that's all. We're okay.'

The look on Sean's face says he knows I'm lying.

Other than the girls and Diane, we don't have visitors. Sean would rather not see people, and I understand why. He won't want sympathy, would prefer to be remembered for how he was, how he used to be. I've told friends and relatives not to contact us, that I'll be in touch when I need to.

Chris and Bill have a case packed. They'll be here at the drop of a hat if I ask them. A few days ago I rang them saying

Sean was near his end, then I had to quickly call them back and tell them he was awake and thinking about coming downstairs.

I didn't expect Eve to ring me, or to mention the name I would rather forget. She wanted to ask me if I'd let David know when Sean dies and that he'd like to be there at the funeral. She reminded me it was David who urged Diane to let Sean stay with me, which is something I haven't forgotten.

I take the cigarette from Sean's fingers. He opens his eyes. 'Do you want to finish this?' I say, handing it back to him.

He takes the cigarette. Smoke curls from his mouth. 'You'll need money. There's some, but it might not be enough for my...' He's avoiding my eyes. Avoids the word – "funeral".

'We're not hard up,' I say in a tone that sounds as though we're discussing whether we can afford a takeaway or not. 'What with my wages and the rent from the houses...'

Ignoring what I said, he tells me, 'My sickness benefit is paid into Diane's bank account. I'm not spending much so there'll be some there.'

He takes a drag from the cigarette. I wait for him to speak again. 'Diane was very good to me. I'd like you two to be friends. She'll need support. It won't be easy. She hasn't any family to speak of. There's a brother, but she doesn't see much of him.'

'I'll do my best. I promise.'

'What are you going to do about Ireland?'

'I'll go back.'

'Make the garden beautiful again. Think of me when you're there.'

A day won't go by without me thinking of him.

This morning he asked me to take Lily from his room. He said the weight of her body on his legs made it difficult to move, and she is such a small cat.

'Chris,' I say, when she answers the phone. 'I think you'd better come. It won't be much longer.'

CHAPTER 35

I've given Chris and Bill my bedroom. They can't be asleep. Sean's screams will be sure to wake them. The drama started late this afternoon, when Sean developed severe abdominal pains. I called the surgery; a young locum came to the house. He gave Sean an injection of morphine and the pain eased. He also gave me the telephone number of the Macmillan nurses.

It was a good two hours after the locum left that Chris, Bill and I heard the crash. I flew up the stairs; Sean was on the bathroom floor. I helped him up, walked with him to his room and saw him into bed. Despite his exhaustion, he told me he'd had terrible diarrhoea and had to check he'd cleaned the bathroom properly – I did; it was spotless. The pain was back with a vengeance. Frantic with worry, I rang Macmillan nurses. They told me they'd be with us as soon as possible and then rang back to say they needed to go to another hospital to pick up a morphine pump.

I've turned the heating off but sweat is pouring from Sean's face. I feel helpless. Sean's pain rips through my body with each cry he makes.

I ring the nurse again. 'We're on our way,' they say.

I turn to Sean. 'They're coming.' I pick up the cold wet flannel and wipe the sweat from his face, willing the nurses to hurry.

I hear the welcome sound of a vehicle; I look out of the window, run downstairs and open the door.

Two nurses follow me to Sean's room. I watch them unpack what must be the pump. The older nurse is rolling up Sean's pyjama sleeve. The younger nurse is putting the plug into a socket. She straightens up and says, 'I'll go and park.' I hear Sean say, 'There's not much flesh,' and I watch the needle from the pump go into Sean's arm.

The nurse sits on the edge of Sean's bed. 'I'm sorry we took so long,' she says. 'There's a shortage of pumps.' She waits for a few minutes, then asks, 'How are you feeling now?'

He closes his eyes. 'Better.'

She looks at me. 'If he needs it you can increase the dosage by pressing this button.' I walk over and look to where she points.

The younger nurse comes back into the room. 'How are things?' she asks.

For a few minutes we watch Sean. His eyes are closed.

'We'll be going now,' whispers the older nurse. 'He won't feel anymore pain.'

I follow them downstairs – Angels have crossed our path and I don't want to lose them.

I go into Sean's room. His eyes are open. The green light on the pump reassures me that for the moment the machine is working.

I take the chair to Sean's bed. 'I could do with a cigarette,' he says.

I gather the tobacco and Rizlas from the bedside table, roll and light a cigarette.

He takes it from me, saying, 'Don't leave me.'

'I won't. I'm staying right here with you.'

'I'm frightened,' he says.

I take his hand, thinking, 'So am I.'

I've lost track of time, whether I've been sat holding Sean's hand for one hour or two. The cold night air penetrates my bones. I think about my duvet downstairs on the sofa. Sean is in a deep sleep; gently, I take my hand from his.

I carry the duvet to Sean's room. Wrap it around me and lie on the floor. The green light on the pump is like a magnet.

The machine's low drone tells me it's working but my eyes keep going to it, as if not looking at it will court disaster.

Daylight arrives. I stand up from the floor, hugging the duvet to me. I go to Sean's bed. He is breathing, but that is all. There will be no more sharing bottles of wine and rolling cigarettes. No more parties. No more moments together.

CHAPTER 36

If anyone should ask me who else was at the funeral, in all honesty I'd have to say I don't know. A few individuals stood out like characters in a film, but the majority were no more than cardboard cut-outs. I walked through the crematorium doors into the chapel as though from the wings onto a stage; all eyes turned towards me and I was the leading player.

I remember seeing David's face and Eve with her arm through his, the smiles of sympathy and encouragement from my close friends, my daughters with eyes red from crying, Bill's heart-wrenching sobs, Chris's words of comfort, Diane in the background, her black hair and black coat a dark contrast to the white wall behind her.

Another scene: Adam, Sam and I are stood waiting behind a white van, watching as a man in a navy T-shirt opens the back doors – a white van is an unorthodox hearse but so was the bright sweater I was wearing, its confectionery blue and green stripes as unconventional as our jeans and the ring through the undertaker's nose.

I remember the weight of the coffin on my shoulder and wondering why Sean's skeletal body could be so heavy. And then, as though in a dream, the coffin had been placed on a pedestal and I was listening to an old friend of Sean's give a eulogy. He spoke of escapades from their youth; a smile escaped my lips. A tear ran a slow journey down my face when someone read John Masefield's poem "Sea Fever".

As we left the chapel, I stopped at the coffin, saying a silent goodbye, not moving until my sister touched my arm, whispered, 'Come on, love,' and I took her hand, leaving Sean to make his final departure the way he would have wanted – alone.

The last act required no more than thanking Blodwyn for preparing the food, shaking hands, receiving cards and kisses of condolence. A man introduced himself as Diane's brother. I was surprised how nice he was.

Sean's parents, my sister and brother-in-law were on their way home when the musicians arrived, carrying fiddles, whistles, guitars and banjos. Music filled the house and I thought, 'There can't be music, not without Sean.' I left them playing their instruments, went up to my room, took Sean's bottle of sleeping tablets from my bedside drawer, swallowed one tablet and then another.

When I woke it was midday. The house was completely silent. I got out of bed, and Lily followed me downstairs. The glasses and dishes were washed. Everything put back in place. The party is over and I've a thousand sorries with nowhere to go.

CHAPTER 37

Sean asked me to befriend Diane. He said it would be difficult but I made a promise and I intended to keep it. After rehearsing and re-rehearsing what I'm going to say, I picked up the phone. Diane answered straightaway; surprisingly, she agreed to meet me. I suggest seeing her outside the Royal Oak because of its proximity to us both.

Diane is waiting outside the pub. I give a wave and hurry across the road. She looks at her wrist-watch, scowls and says, 'You're late.'

I pull my phone from my pocket and glance at the time. 'I thought we said seven-thirty.'

'It's seven-thirty-two,' she says, striding towards the pub door, pushing it open, leaving it to swing shut behind her.

I follow after her. The huge bar-room is a mass of empty tables. 'You sit down,' I tell her. 'I'll get the drinks. What are you having?'

'Slimline tonic, lemon and no ice.' – I was hoping she would choose something stronger, something that might soothe her temper.

The only other people in the pub are two elderly men talking to the barman. I go to the bar; the barman leaves his companions and quickly serves me.

I take the drinks to where Diane is sitting. 'Sorry, no lemon,' I tell her.

'I'm not surprised. It always was a dump; it's only ever catered for boozers.'

'I thought you wanted to come here.'

'Only because you insisted.'

'I suggested it because it's handy for us both.' I take a sip of wine, wondering what I can say to help the evening run more smoothly. 'I'm back to work tomorrow,' I tell her. 'It's hard to believe the funeral was over a week ago.'

I wait for her to say something. 'How are you?' I ask.

She gives me a hard stare and says, 'Call it a funeral?'

'What do you mean?'

'What do I mean? It was disgusting, an insult to Sean's name. God knows what everyone thought.'

'It's what Sean would have wanted. Years ago, he told me he didn't want any priest saying prayers over him.'

'You can have a decent funeral without a priest. God! That punk of an undertaker, you in jeans and that awful jumper. I even heard his body arrived in a white van. Have you no respect for the dead?'

'Sean hated formality. I told you, it's what he would have wanted. I planned the funeral the way he...'

'FUNERAL!' she shouts.

I glance at the men at the bar. They have stopped talking; all three of them are looking at us. 'Keep your voice down,' I tell her.

'I'll talk as loud as I like. I've nothing to hide. That funeral was a travesty, a mockery; he deserved better than that. He left you enough; three houses and God knows what in the bank. I got nothing. I brought him back from Ireland, nursed him, for what? NOTHING!'

'He wouldn't have wanted a hearse, or his coffin being carried by men in black. It had nothing to do with money, even though there's very little in the bank. My wages dropped considerably when I started working from home. In fact, Sean was worried about me having to pay for the funeral. He thought there might be some change left from his sickness benefit. He told me it was paid into your bank account.'

Leaving her drink untouched, she stands up, saying, 'You're the limit. I gave Sean every penny of his benefit. You're deceitful and a liar. Yes, that's what you are, a liar.

You and David have been up to no good for years. I suspected there was someone else when I was with him. That someone was you! I told Sean David wasn't the only one you were playing around with, there were bound to be others. You and David were a good match!'

I shake my head, stunned by what she's saying. 'It's not true,' I say as she walks away and the door closes behind her.

I drain the last drop of wine from my glass, turn to the men at the bar and say, 'I hope you enjoyed the entertainment.' With all the dignity I can muster I put my glass down and wish them goodnight.

The meeting with Diane has upset me in so many ways. I want to keep my promise to Sean but how can I when Diane so obviously dislikes me. I worry that Sean believed the things she told him. My selfish, stupid, infatuation; everything that's happened, has been caused by me. There wouldn't have been a Diane if I hadn't left Sean.

I stand outside the day centre, wondering if it will be possible to go through the day without seeing or speaking to any of the staff or clients – the last thing I want is a sympathy I don't deserve. Bracing myself, I put on a brave face and go into the building.

Thankfully, most people stay away from my office, leaving me to get on with my work on my own – people don't know what to say when it comes to death. At lunchtime I remain where I am. I'm about to take my sandwich from my bag when the door opens – I guessed Vicky would come looking for me – she sits in the chair next to me and asks, 'How are you?'

'Okay.'

'Did you see Diane?'

'Yes.'

'How did it go?'

'Not good. I upset her and things went from bad to worse.'

'You must be feeling rotten. Give it time, it's early days. Things will get better.'

'I don't know how. I hate myself for what I did. What I caused.'

'Anna! You must stop this.'

'I can't even keep the promise I made. Diane's never going to let me be her friend. Though there's one thing I can do. Sean loved the house in Ireland. As soon as this job's finished I'm going home.' I stop speaking. For a minute I think about what I had said; the word "home" and what it means to me. 'That's what I'm going to do, I'm going home. Sean never did finish some of the jobs he'd started. But I'll get them finished. I'll make the house beautiful. The garden will be as it was before I left. It's what he would want me to do.'

My decision to go back to Ireland certainly lifts my spirit. I arrive back from work, determined to get myself into a better state of mind. Going over what Liz taught me about visualisation, I unplug the phone, remove Lily from the room, take off my shoes, lie on the bed and close my eyes.

I look up at the bedroom ceiling, transfixed by what has happened. I've been transported back into my room as quickly and mysteriously as I left it. The images of where I've been and what happened sit clearly in my mind. Sean's face free from pain. The deserted, flat, ochre-coloured land stretching as far and wide as my eye can see. The warmth of Sean's arms around me, feeling the softness of his sweater. His backward step, the gentle way he moved my arms away from him, saying, 'It's not your time,' and the moment I knew I was about to lose him.

The following day, I hurry home from work, take Lily from my bed, lie down and close my eyes.

My eye takes me over the ochre land to Sean, a distant figure with his arms held high, waving a joyous goodbye.
The following day, I hurry home, take Lily from my bed and lie down.

The deserted ochre land stretches as far and wide as my eye can see.

CHAPTER 38

I'm beginning to wish I hadn't rung Liz; she's adamant that my meeting with Sean, the strange place I found myself in, was a dream. 'You've been terribly stressed,' she says. 'Stress affects the mind in all sorts of ways. You needed Sean's arms around you, you needed a loving goodbye and your mind gave it to you.'

'But it was all so real. I felt his body, his warmth. I was with him; in that place.'

'It was a dream, Anna.'

'It didn't feel like dreaming. It didn't feel like visualisation. You know better than I do how long it takes to reach a deeply relaxed state of mind, and you always know where you are. This time was different. I lay on the bed and there I was: with Sean, in that strange place, touching him, holding him, wanting to go where he was going. That's another thing; you know I'm not religious. I don't believe in heaven or hell, but I knew without a doubt that he was going to a glorious place, a place so splendid it's beyond our understanding.'

'Anna, my love, it was a dream. You were upset. You need to start getting your life back. When was the last time you went out, and I'm not talking about you meeting Diane?'

'I go to Alice's every Sunday for lunch. Kate and I meet up about once a week, sometimes at hers, sometimes mine.'

'That's your kids. I mean spending a bit of time with your mates. Listen, come round to me this Saturday. I'll cook us a meal. I'll invite Vicky and Sue.'

'That'll be lovely. I'll look forward to it.'

'Come about seven.'

'Yes, see you then. I put the phone down, unconvinced that where I'd been and what I'd seen had been a dream.

Liz ushers me into the sitting-room then dashes into the kitchen. Sue and Vicky are sat at the table. 'Sorry I'm late,' I say, putting a bottle of wine next to the half empty one already there. 'I've been talking to Bridie, my neighbour in Ireland. I don't know if Vicky told you,' I say as I sit next to her, 'but when my job comes to an end I'm going home, I'm going to Ireland.'

Liz comes back into the room holding a pair of oven-gloves, stands at the end of the table, saying, 'Yes, she's been telling us, but what about your house here? What do your girls think about you going?'

'They know I've got to go back some time. Nobody's been to the house since Sean left. I can't just leave it.'

'You said home – does that mean you'll be staying in Ireland?' asks Sue.

'It certainly feels like going home, but I think I need to be there a while before I make any big decisions.'

'Have you decided what you're going to do with the house in Wellington Road?' persists Liz.

'I've been giving it a bit of thought. I don't want to move Lily until I'm settled and I don't know when that's going to be. I'm thinking about looking for a lodger, someone who'll keep an eye on the cat and the house while I'm away.'

Liz and Sue's eyes turn to Vicky. Vicky looks at me and says, 'Craig wants to sell the house. He's asked me to put it on the market. I suppose it's time to move on. I can't afford to run it on my own. Anyway, I'm looking for a place to rent.'

'Vicky!' I say, delighted. 'This could be the answer to both our problems. Why didn't you mention it before? I'd love you to move in with me. I've been worried about leaving Lily with a stranger. I can't think of a better solution for either of us.'

'How much will the rent be?'

'Don't worry about that. We'll come to some agreement, something that suits us both. Anyway, I'll be getting my old age pension next month. I'll be rolling in it. The room's yours, Vicky. Move in whenever you're ready.'

'What I want to know,' says Liz waving the oven-glove, 'is why Anna hasn't complained about her empty glass. Someone pour her a drink while I get the chicken out of the oven. I think we should start celebrating now.'

Vicky's been with me for over a fortnight. Since she arrived, her chatter and music – seventies pop – has filled the air, chased the memories of haunting jigs and airs, cigarettes and wine, out of the house. She's filled the empty space between getting up and going to work; coming home and going to bed, those times when I found myself out in the garden, thinking about Sean, picturing him wearing his old grey dressing gown, meticulously sweeping the path.

Some might say, "What about Ireland; you'll be on your own there." They're right, I will be on my own, but I'll be busy. I'm going to make the house beautiful, bring the garden back to how it was before I left, finish what we started, find the perfect spot to put Sean's ashes and make amends.

I thought I couldn't deal with other people's misery. How wrong I was. I'm more than able to throw myself into a sorrowful story – it makes my own tale of woe far more bearable – I ignore the paper-thin wall that divides my office from reception. Don't give a damn who overhears me telling clients and carers the name and address of the solicitor who supports us. I print copies of clients' files, hand them to Steve as though they're nothing but postage stamps. So it comes as no surprise when I'm called into Margaret's office and she tells me, 'I've had a call from head office. I've been told to tell you that, as from now, your employment with us has ceased. I'm sorry; I didn't want you to leave this way.' She stops talking, glances towards the door, and in a quiet voice says, 'You and Steve and everybody else involved are fighting a losing battle. You can't beat Social Services; there's far more of them than there are of you.'

'We haven't lost yet. There'll be a reprieve.'

'I hope you're right. I'm sorry this has had to happen, but I've been told to tell you to collect your belongings and leave right now.'

'I'll get my stuff together but, before I do, I'd like to thank you for your support, for allowing me to work from home when Sean was so ill.'

'I was glad to help. I'm sorry you're going. These are sad times.'

'Not if Steve and the others have their way. I won't tell you the details, but I think, very soon, you'll find a nice surprise in your mail box.'

She gives me a weary smile and I say, 'I'll be going back to Ireland a little sooner than I anticipated, and I'm really looking to it.'

Alice opens the door, looks at me in surprise, saying, 'Mum! Aren't you supposed to be at work?'

'Not anymore,' I say, going into the house. 'I've just had the sack.'

'Oh my God! Tell me, what's happened?'

I follow her into the kitchen. Stella runs over to me and shows me her doll. I pick her up, carry her to the table and sit with her on my lap.

Alice puts the kettle on as I tell her, 'It was to be expected. I wasn't exactly hiding the fact that I was helping the protestors. Anyway, I'll be able to leave for Ireland whenever I like; I thought soon after my birthday.'

Still holding on to the doll, Stella begins to wriggle. I help her to the floor and she runs from the room. Alice puts a cup of tea in front of me, saying, 'Kate and I don't like the thought of you going to Ireland on your own. We want to be with you. Adam's happy to take a few days off work and look after the girls. Kate said she's due some holiday time.'

Hearing a rumble of wheels, we look round. Stella has put the doll into her pram. 'I'll get your coat,' says Alice. 'You can take dolly for a walk in the garden.' She goes into the hallway and comes back with the coat. Putting Stella's arms through the coat sleeves, she looks at me and asks, 'Do you think Bridie will mind having a couple of extra guests for a few nights? You told me she'd offered to let you stay with her till the house is warm and dry again.'

Without waiting for an answer, Alice opens the back door and helps Stella out with her pram. Coming back in, she exclaims, 'Hey, what's the matter? Why are your crying? I thought you'd be pleased.' She puts her arm around me. 'Come on, tell me. What's upset you? Is it losing your job? Is it going away?'

'No. I want to go to Ireland.'

'What is it then?'

'It's silly, but I can't seem to stop crying. Everyone's so kind. Vicky's an angel. She can't do enough for me. All my friends are so supportive. Jenny rings most evenings. And you and Kate, well, your offer to come with me! I really don't deserve it.'

'What do you mean, you don't deserve it?'

'I don't. Not after what I did. The hurt I caused. He wouldn't have become ill. He wouldn't have died if I hadn't... I might as well have held a gun to his head and pulled the trigger.'

'MUM! You must stop this. You aren't helping any of us saying things like that. Dad's lifestyle killed him. NOT YOU!'

I immediately close my mouth. Zip my lips from forming the words – stress can cause cancer. Instead I say, 'I'm sorry. I'm glad you're coming. We should do this together. We should take Sean's ashes to his home, together, as a family. That's what he would have wanted.'

She gives me a hug. 'So, we'll go after your birthday.' She looks at a brightly coloured wall calendar. 'Let's see... That'll be just over four weeks away.' Sitting next to me, she says, 'You really must try to get it into your head that it's not your fault. Dad was on his own self-destructive journey.'

Feeling her eyes looking at me, I stare down at the table. 'Maybe it wasn't a dream,' she says. 'Maybe Dad was telling you he's all right. He's okay. He wanted you to know he loves you and he knew you loved him.' She takes a deep breath. 'He's gone, Mum – let him go. Don't keep worrying and fretting. Put away the baggage, it's weighing you down. Dad would want you to go to your new life the way he went to his, with a joyous wave.'

I lift my head. 'I will, but it's early days. I'll be better as time goes by. I promise.'

Alice stands up, looks out of the window, opens the door, shouting, 'Stella! Don't play with mud,' and goes into the garden.

I pick up a framed photograph of Sean. It was taken when Alice, Adam and the children were staying with us in Ireland. Sean is pushing Ella on the swing he'd made. Directing my thoughts to his smiling face, I send him a silent message. 'I'm not ready for another life. Not yet. Not until I've made my peace with this one and with you.'

CHAPTER 39

I step into the house, calling, 'Hello,' take the key from the lock, put it back into my purse, thinking Vicky must be out. I look into the hall mirror wondering what she'll think of my new haircut, the highlighted layers – the visit to the hairdresser was a present from Kate; she always has such good ideas when it comes to buying presents. A voucher to spend in Bristol's most exclusive hair salon was not only a lovely surprise, it was a much-needed reminder that I'd been seriously neglecting my appearance.

A faint sound makes me look towards the kitchen. The kitchen door is closed, which is curious as we always leave it open to give Lily access into the rest of the house.

I leave the mirror and open the kitchen door. My mouth drops open as a chorus of Happy Birthday greets me. Putting my bag onto the floor, I look at the smiling faces in front of me – Alice, Adam, Kate, Sam, Ella, Stella, Vicky, Jenny, Liz with her arm through a forty-something good-looking man, and Blodwyn wearing a short, tight, bright pink dress.

Silver and gold balloons hang from the ceiling. A "60 Today" banner is pinned to the wall, a pile of presents on a chair beneath it. The table is almost trembling with the weight of food and bottles of wine.

Ella runs towards me shouting, 'Surprise, surprise!' Stella follows behind her calling, 'Prise, prise.'

Alice puts her arm around me. 'Happy Birthday, Mum. We thought it was better having a party here than in a restaurant."

'Gosh! What a shock,' I say, taking my coat off. 'I never expected this; how did you manage to...'

'By sending you to the hairdresser,' she says as she takes my coat from me. 'Your hair looks great. Do you like it?'

'I love it.'

'Happy Birthday, sis.'

'Jenny! Come here. Let me give you a hug. It's so good to see you. How did you get here?'

'On the train. I've got a day return. I wouldn't miss my big sister's sixtieth, would I.'

'Chris and granddad would have come,' says Kate, 'but granddad's not well. She sends their apologies."

'He's not been well since Sean died. I'll give them a ring in the morning.'

'I love your hair, Anna. What would you like to drink?' asks Sue.

'A glass of wine will be lovely.'

'That hair style really suits you,' says Liz. She turns to the man at her side. 'This is Ian; I hope you don't mind me bringing him.'

'Of course not. Nice to meet you, Ian.'

'You too. Can I get you a drink... some food?'

'Sue's getting me a drink. I'll have something to eat after I've opened my presents.'

'Thanks, Sue... Cava! Lovely.'

'We know how much you like it.'

'I'm going to open my presents.'

'We'll help you, Nana.'

'Stella! Don't throw the paper everywhere. Ella, take the presents into the sitting-room and put them on the coffee table. Thank you, darling.'

'Thank you, everyone. I don't know what else to say. You've all been so generous.'

'Your food, Anna. I got a bit of everything.'

'Thanks Ian.'

'Nana, can we play outside?'

'Of course; ask Mummy to unlock the door.'

'I love your hair; it suits you shorter.'

'Thanks, Blodwyn; it's my birthday present from Kate.'

'Oh my God. What a beautiful cake. Where did it come from?'

'Blodwyn made it.'

'Blodwyn! Thank you. You're amazing.'

'You're welcome, babe.'

'Let me top up your glass. We're going to have a toast.'

'Adam, call the children. We're going to light the candles. Hold on, Kate. Let's wait for the children.'

'Nana! Blow out the candles.'

'Make a wish.'

'A toast to Anna.'

'Fill her glass – it's empty!'

'To Anna.'

'Thank you, everyone. I don't know what to say. I'm stunned; I didn't expect a party.'

'We wanted to say goodbye as well as happy birthday.'

'When are you going?'

'Thursday. Five days' time.'

'How long are you going for?'

'I don't know yet.'

'You'll miss the family.'

'I will. I'll miss you all.'

'We're going to miss you.'

'Would you like another drink?'

'Yes, please.'

'It's getting dark. I'll switch the light on.'

'Do you know how long you'll be away?'

'No, I don't. Not yet. I need to give it a while.'

'We'll be off now, Mum. It's way past the children's bedtime.'

'What time is it? God! Is it that late?'

'I must be going as well, Anna. My old man will be wondering what I'm up to.'

'Thanks for everything, Blodwyn. Like all my friends, I don't know what I'd have done without you.'

'Oh Anna. Don't cry, babe.'

'I'm not. It's just that you're all so kind and I've drunk too much.'

'I'd better go as well, Anna. I need to catch the 9.25 train. Sue's going to give me a lift to the station.'

'Well, it's on my way and I don't want to be late. I'm driving to Dorset early in the morning. Mum hasn't been too good.'

'Sam and I are going. We're meeting friends in the Prince of Wales. Do you fancy joining us, Mum?'

'Thanks, but I don't think so. I've drunk enough already.'

'Do you mind if Ian and I tag along with you?'

'Not at all. What about you, Vicky?'

'Not tonight. I'm going to make Anna a cup of black coffee and put my feet up.'

'I hope you all come and visit me; I'd love to show you Ireland.'

'We will.'

'Bye, Mum.'

'Bye, Anna."

'Goodnight.'

'Goodbye.'

'Bon Voyage.'

CHAPTER 40

I look back to the day when I first saw this house, remembering a cloudless sky, the warmth of the sun, Blackie cautiously coming to greet us. I thought the weather and the dog were an omen; I truly believed Sean and I would be happy living here. Today there is a different picture – a blanket of clouds blend with the landscape, creating one grey smudge. The excitement I held then is now one of sadness.

Alice's voice reminds me I'm not alone. 'What do you want to do, Mum? Shall we go in now or go to Bridie's and come back later?'

I stare at the house; the weight of weather and neglect has left its mark. Rain has lashed the colour from the door, curtains as limp as dishcloths hang at the windows, drips from a broken gutter have fallen like tears, leaving a trail of green algae. Like me, the house is grieving. 'I want to go in now.'

Kate gives the door a hefty shove and it opens. Two brown envelopes lie on the porch floor – I expected a reminder to tax the car to be waiting for me; when Sean and Diane were last here they were unaware he would never come back. The second envelope is so damp I have to scrape it from the floor with my nails. Sean's name catches my breath – when he died I expected the world to know. I open the envelope; the television licence had been due last summer.

Each room tells a story – Sean and Diane had left in a hurry. On the table is an empty carrier bag, an unwashed baked-bean tin, teabags, a carton of sour milk, plastic food wrapping and two, hardly touched, mugs of cold tea covered in mould. The stench is nauseating. Alice opens a window. I go to the sink and turn off the dripping tap with hardly a look at the unwashed dishes.

I climb the stairs to the bedroom wondering what I will find. On the unmade bed is a black plastic bin bag. I look inside – in their rush to leave, they never thought for one minute I'd be the one to find their dirty underwear.

Everywhere gives a picture, pieces together the last days they spent in this house – a Catherine Cookson paperback left open in the sitting-room, the scented soap in the bathroom, a pair of pink fluffy slippers on the stairs – each item a reminder that Sean's last days in this house were spent with Diane.

Telling myself that Sean's ashes are more precious to me than anything Diane and Sean may have done together, I go outside and take the urn from the car boot. Holding the urn with both hands, I look for a perfect place to put it.

Most of the garden is hidden beneath a blanket of couch grass and dock leaves. Only the rowan tree we planted when we first moved here has survived. Despite neglect and fierce winds it stands tall and straight; new buds are beginning appear. A length of twine is caught in a blackthorn bush. Putting the urn down, I untangle it, move away some of the weeds and tie the urn to the rowan's slender trunk.

The girls have been so busy they don't ask what I've been doing. Cupboards and drawers have been emptied; rubbish has been put into carrier-bags.

'The place needs a good scrub,' says Kate, 'but there're hardly any cleaning materials. Not only that, it's bloody freezing in here!'

'I agree,' I say. 'Let's go to Bridie's. We'll get what we need tomorrow. I'll tax the car while we're there.'

Bridie is sat at her window. She gives a wave, stands at her door as I park the car, her smile as lovely as ever.

'Welcome, welcome,' she says.

I throw my arms around her. 'I'm so pleased to see you.'

'I'm glad you've come home.'

'You've met the girls,' I say, turning towards Alice and Kate.

'Yes, welcome. You're Kate and you're Alice, is that right?'

'You've a good memory,' says Kate. 'It was a few summers ago when Mum and Dad were living in the house.'

'I'm sorry about Sean. I was shocked to hear he'd died. God rest his soul. He'll be in peace now. Anyway, why are we standing out here? Come in.'

'We might as well get the bags while we're here,' I say going to the car and opening the boot. 'It'll save coming out later.'

The little bungalow is how I remember it. Like Bridie, it emits a feeling of peace. Despite my agnostic leanings, the holy water and religious symbols that adorn the walls is oil on troubled water.

We follow Bridie to our rooms. 'The girls are in the back bedroom next to mine,' she says.

'You're in here, Anna.' She opens a door and I look into a plainly furnished room, the only adornment on the bare walls a Palm Cross. A swathe of net curtain gives a cloudy view of the Cinquecento parked outside the window.

'I hope you'll be comfortable. You know where the bathroom is. When you're ready, I'll be in the kitchen. I bet you could do with a cup of tea.'

After two or three cups of tea comes Irish stew. The more we eat the more the huge ladle replenishes our bowls. When the stew pot is empty, we're invited into the lounge to watch television – a concert by three Irish tenors. Bridie continues to serve food – chunks of sweet, bright pink cake and yet more cups of tea. The girls look exhausted and I can hardly keep my eyes open. As soon as the tenors take their final bow, before Bridie can offer more tea, cake or biscuits, I stand up saying, 'If you don't mind, I think I'll go to bed; it's been a long day and we've a lot to do tomorrow.'

As though waiting for the cue, both Kate and Alice stand up saying they are also tired. Declining Bridie's offer of cocoa, we say goodnight and go to our rooms. The last thing I remember before falling asleep is holding the hot water bottle that had been put between the flannelette sheets.

A noise claws its way into my dream. A flashing light forces its way through my eyelids. For a second I wonder where I am, then I open my eyes. The noise, the flashing light is coming from outside. I quickly get out of bed and pull back the curtain. The car is behaving as though it is alive. The noise from the horn and the flashing headlights synchronize, invading the night like some mad carnival.

I run out of the bedroom, down the passage to the front door. Finding it locked, I run to the back door; that is also locked.

I rush into the girl's room and shake them awake. 'Something's happening. It's the car. It's as if it's alive. The horn's loud enough to wake the dead and the headlights are flashing. I need to get to it but I can't; the door's locked.'

The girls get out of bed, hurry to my room and look out of the window. 'We'll have to wake Bridie,' says Alice.

Bridie tells me where the keys are. I run to the scullery and take them from the little cupboard by the door. The girls follow me outside. 'The door's open,' exclaims Kate, pointing to the driver's door. 'It set the alarm off.'

I slam the door shut and the night falls silent. 'But how? I didn't even know the car had an alarm.'

'Someone must have been walking past, saw the car and thought they'd...' says Kate.

'Who on earth would be walking around at this time of night? We're in the middle of nowhere.'

'Perhaps you didn't shut the door properly and the wind blew it open,' insists Kate.

'There is no wind. I'm sure I shut the door. If I hadn't, why didn't it go off then?'

'You did shut the door,' says Alice. 'I remember checking. Perhaps Dad's letting us know he's with us.'

I shake my head, telling myself there has to be an explanation, but I can't think what that might be.

CHAPTER 41

Saying goodbye to Alice and Kate was torture. I missed them from the moment they disappeared into the departure lounge. All the way back from the airport, I was dreading this moment, the moment I walk into this house alone.

When the girls were with me my mind was set on the future. Now they've gone I think back to the past; my life with Sean. Sean had had his problems but I was no help; in fact my refusal to be anywhere near pleasant, my discontent and disapproval had made things much, much worse.

The girls had put a bit of life into the house. If they hadn't been here when I found the cardboard box, when I opened it and discovered a half empty packet of Viagra and a penis-shaped vibrator, I would have been inconsolable. As it was, they started laughing and so did I. Though even they couldn't shift me from the upset I felt when I found the Christmas parcel and read the gift-tag. The present was to me from Bill and Chris. I don't know how many months had passed before he told them I'd left him. He never believed I would go for good – I don't know what I'm going to do with the jumper; I don't think I'll ever be able to wear it.

I sort through Sean's clothes, fold them neatly and place them on the back of the kitchen chair – they are work clothes, ripped in places, marked with plaster and spotted with paint. Like the boots on the floor beside them, they bear the marks of his trade.

On the table is an assembly of the things he loved. Other than his fiddle and a couple of music books, there's nothing of any value. But the scratched CDs and records, the stained and torn sheets of music were an important part of his life, as important as the clothes he worked in.

I hear my name and look around. Mary is standing at the open door. 'I hope I'm not disturbing you,' she says, coming into the kitchen. 'I saw your car and wondered how you're getting on. I thought you might need a bit of company now the girls have gone.'

'That's nice of you. I'm okay. There's so much to do here, I haven't time for moping... I was wondering what to do with Sean's old work clothes.'

'If there's anything you want to throw away, use my bin; it gets emptied tomorrow.'

'I can't do that.' Sean's love of music, his work clothes, those old boots were a part of his life – I suddenly remember the sack of dirty underwear, the vibrator and Viagra – 'Though, I do have a couple of things I need to dispose of. Do you know anyone who might want the fiddle?' I ask, taking it from its case. 'I brought it with us because it needs to be here, in Ireland, being played by someone who loves the music.'

'What about the girls? Won't they want it?'

'Kate plays a flute. She prefers it to the fiddle. Alice never wanted to play an instrument.'

'What about your grandchildren?'

'I thought about them, but the chances are they won't be interested. It will be forgotten, left in the back of a cupboard, never to be played again. Here's the place to find someone who'll play it.'

'My children have their own fiddles. Most people who play have their own instruments, but I do know someone... if you're sure?'

'I am. Who is it?'

'A boy; he's about eleven. His music teacher says he's quite exceptional. The fiddle he uses belongs to the school. His family won't be able to give you much; the boy's one of six. His father can't work; a drunk driver ran into him and he's now paraplegic.'

'Give it to him,' I say putting the fiddle back into its case. 'I don't want any money. If they want to give something they can make a donation to a cancer charity.'

'He'll be so pleased,' she says, pulling the case towards her.

'Would you like a drink?'

'Just a quick one,' she says, sitting down. 'I said I'd pop in to see Tom's mum. She's had a hip replacement. She came out of hospital yesterday.'

'How is she?' I ask while filling the kettle.

'She's grand, but what about you? What are your plans? Is there anything Tom and I can help you with?'

I put tea-bags into two mugs and stand waiting for the kettle to boil, saying, 'That's good of you. There's so much to do, I'm not sure where to start. There's still work on the house that needs finishing. Then there's the garden and Sean's car.' I go to the window and look out at the old Ford, now green with mould, its tyres completely flat. 'I must get it removed.' I turn back to face her. 'I need to employ someone to give me a hand.'

The kettle boils and I fill the mugs. 'I might make a start on the outbuildings,' I say, putting a mug of tea in front of her and sitting down. 'There's a lot of junk, but most of Sean's tools are in good condition; somebody might want them.'

'Tom knows everyone,' she says. 'He'll be able to recommend someone who'll give you a hand. I'm sure if you put an ad in the local paper you'll get a buyer for of some of the tools. If you need anything taken to the tip, we've the trailer. How are you getting on at Bridie's?'

'Fine. I've put on a few pounds since I've been staying with her. Now the house is warm and dry, I'll be moving back. It's going to feel strange living here on my own.' I contemplate the future. 'It's as though a great chunk of it is missing. I won't see the girls again until August, when we scatter Sean's ashes.'

For a moment we sit in silence, drinking our tea, each in our own thoughts.

'Well, I'd better be going,' she says standing up. She puts the cup onto the draining board then picks up the fiddle-case. 'Thank you for this. That lad will be so pleased.' She goes towards the door then stops and turns to look at me. 'It's great to have you back.' She hesitates – I sense there is something else she wants to say. 'That woman, what was her name? Sean's woman friend.'

I don't reply.

'Diane, that's it, Diane. When Tom told me Sean had a woman in the house, I stayed away. It didn't seem right. He was still your husband, then I met them in town and Sean introduced me. Well, I could barely look at her, let alone speak.'

Quickly changing the subject, I say, 'You might as well have the music books.' Picking up a carrier bag, I go to the dresser, put them into the bag and give them to her. I watch her walk away, all the time thinking what a hypocrite I am, accepting her sympathy as though I deserve it. I should call her back; tell her the truth. Let her know there wouldn't have been a Diane if I hadn't left Sean. But how can I? The thought of losing her friendship, seeing the look of disdain on her face is something I couldn't bear.

I throw armfuls of wood as the flames grow brighter and higher. A shower of orange sparks rise and fall, a wave of heat hits my face. I pick up the tapes, the records and CDs, watch them twist and turn like dancers before they vanish. Sheets of music become fragments, float to the ground like grey confetti. His clothes quench the flames then roar like a dragon; his boots stay fast, glowing like beacons. I wait until the fire dies, until the only recognisable objects on the black circle are two steel toe caps. They are still warm when I pick them up, when I go to the rowan tree, when I lay them on the bed of wild flowers next to the urn.

CHAPTER 42

Hearing Michael call my name, I let go of the stubborn dock root, straighten up and rub my soiled hands on the legs of my overalls. He walks over to me. 'I'll be going now,' he says.

Michael is a tall, slim, handsome man. He could be in his sixties, though his weather-beaten face makes it difficult to determine his age. Ireland has its fair share of bachelor farmers and Michael is one of them – an elder son that inherits the farm while his younger siblings seek more prosperous lives in other countries. He has two sisters living in America; both of them are married with children and grandchildren. His brother leads a comfortable life in a bungalow in Seaton, paid for with money made from the building trade.

Michael's farm is a short distance from here – Bridie pointed it out to me on one of our walks. Like countless other small farms in West Clare, it is a traditional cottage with a couple of boggy acres and a small herd of cattle.

Michael smiles. His eyes are startlingly blue on his bronzed face. 'I've mended the gutter,' he tells me. 'I'd leave it a while before you paint the wall. Give it time to dry out.'

'Thanks, Michael. I'm in no hurry. Are you still happy to be paid at the end of the week? I can get you money now if you prefer.'

'No, Friday's fine. Have you been down to the festival yet?'

I hesitate before answering. One of the reasons Sean and I came here was for the music. The festival had been one of the main attractions, the icing on the cake for Sean. 'No, I haven't. I went into town yesterday, but only to do a bit of shopping.'

'Well, let me know when you're going. I'll buy you a drink. I'll see you tomorrow then.'

Thinking about Sean and the festival, the upset his behaviour had caused, I watch him walk away.

A small movement catches my eye; the little bird has returned. When Michael arrived, the bird had flown away. Now it is perched on the handle of the wheelbarrow, watching me. Whenever I'm in the garden so is the bird. It's become braver by the day, coming closer and closer towards me. I've come to the conclusion that it must be nesting nearby.

I manage to loosen the soil around the dock root, take hold of the root and pull it out. The bird flies onto the newly cleared ground. I put the dock into the wheelbarrow and watch as the little bird searches through the soil, looking for whatever meadow pipits like to eat.

Yes, that's what it is – a meadow pipit; I'd looked through the "Illustrated Book of Birds" to identify him and there he was, my little brown bird with his pale spotted breast, a common bird, so the book says, but not to me; to me, he's rather special. I like having him around; he's good company. He listens to what I say, lets me arrive at my own decisions without interference. Whether that's planning a new flowerbed or debating if I should leave clearing out the outbuildings until the martins have finished nesting. Today, the question is whether to go to the festival or not. I look at the bird. 'I might even enjoy myself,' I say. 'I need to meet more people. Bridie, Mary, Tom and Michael are the only ones I talk to, and you, of course.' I stick my fork in the ground, 'Yes, that's what I'll do; I'll go to the festival and listen to some music!'

I park the car in the little council estate. The festival started yesterday. Since then even more tents have arrived. I walk into town. Shops that had been closed since the last festival are back in business. On the street, unfamiliar faces outnumber familiar. I look around me, wondering which pub to go into. In the end I decide on Marian's.

The last time I was at the festival, I was with Sean. Marian's was a place where people went to listen to singers; as Sean was only interested in instrumental music, we'd given it a miss.

Marian's is packed. Not wanting to fight my way to the bar, I stand with my back against the wall, listening to the lovely voice singing "Trouble in the Fields". Trying to get a glimpse of the singer, I stand on tiptoe and see a girl with red curly hair, then two men stop in front of me and she is lost from view. I listen to the tragic lyrics until a round of applause signals the end of the song and a rush to the bar; it's then that I decide to leave.

I stand outside, wondering where to go next. The nearest pub is Mulligans, and I cross the road. The pub is busy, but there are a few empty seats. I buy a glass of lemonade then ask a young couple if I can share their table. Their eyes are fixed on something that is happening in the far corner; they turn to look at me. 'Help yourself,' says the man.' I follow their gaze. Four men are deep in conversation. On the table there is a guitar, flute, bodhran and fiddle.

I turn to the girl when she says, 'We heard this guy playing a fiddle in Blondie's last night; he's superb.' I look back at the men, watching them as they pick up their instruments. The man holding the fiddle reminds me of Sean – his looks, the elegant sweep of the bow when it meets the strings, the way he closes his eyes as he sways in time with the music. I recognise the tune straight away – "Carolan's Concerto", one of Sean's favourite pieces. A tear rolls down my cheek and I tell myself I shouldn't be here. I never showed any interest in music when he was alive, so why now?

Desperate to get away, I stand up and push myself through the growing number of people coming into the pub. I feel a hand on my shoulder; someone says my name. For a second I don't recognise him, then Michael says, 'You're not going yet are you? Let me buy you a drink. Are you alright?'

'Yes. No. Thank you, but I must get home. I can't waste the day; there's work to do in the garden.'

'Perhaps another time,' he calls.

As soon as I walk into the house, I feel Sean's spirit. It is everywhere, as though it has become the very house itself. Wherever I look, I see Sean's work: the rendered walls, the tiles on the floor, the kitchen he meticulously designed, and so much more. I hear my voice scream, the uncontrollable sobs as I collapse onto the bottom step of the stairs. When the room falls silent I lift my head, look around me, saying, 'I loved you. We had so much. All the ingredients were there to make our lives perfect. But we blew it, didn't we.'

I don't know how long it's taken for my grief to lay quiet, to notice the patch of blue sky brightening the window. I stand up from the step, open the door to the garden and go outside

I pick up my garden fork; at the same time the little pipit lands on the ground in front of me, almost at my feet. I'm about to start weeding when I change my mind, remembering the fir trees, the brambles invading them like an aggressive army. I put a few more tools into the wheelbarrow and push it to the trees.

It only takes a second to notice the little pipit is perched on a branch of fir – I can't help but wonder why it got here before me; he can hardly read my mind. I reach for my gardening gloves. As I do, something touches the back of my hand, a gentle touch as light as a feather. A second passes and the bird flies to a branch of fir, watches me with small bright eyes. I look at it in amazement. The bird is communicating with me, telling me to get back to what I had been doing because it's hungry. I'm so astonished I have to tell someone.

Alice answers straight away. '...It's been in the garden for weeks,' I say. 'You wouldn't think a wild bird would get that close, would you.'

'How did you feel when it touched you?'

'Good. It was a lovely feeling. It's hard to describe. It was almost like a blessing.'

'Perhaps it was Dad, telling you he's with you.'

'Sean! I don't think so. It was a little bird telling me he's hungry.'

And then she tells me that some cultures believe souls take the form of birds who visit those who grieve for them. I'm about to say, 'I haven't believed in angels since I stopped believing in Father Christmas,' when I change my mind. If it makes her happy to think Sean's a little bird living in my garden, so be it.

I put the phone down, go outside and look up at the sky. The martins are on the wing, clearing the air of insects like small vacuum cleaners. I search for the kestrel who hangs in the sky as still as a hunting cat. I think about Sean and what Alice had said. I can't see Sean as a little nondescript bird, but what would he be? My mind travels to the open land and the lake. Yes, that's what he'd be, a skylark. He would fly high, spread his wings and fill the air with music.

CHAPTER 43

The sea is unusually calm today; two children are jumping the waves, screaming with excitement when the ice cold water catches their feet. I watch them, thinking about my own grandchildren, that they might be with me now if I hadn't left them.

I walk along the shore, gathering shells as I go. It seems hardly yesterday when I was collecting shells with my own children. I cast my mind back, remembering sunny weekends, when spur of the moment decisions made Sean and I thrust the children and tent into the car. We'd head for the Severn Bridge, following the road to the Gower Peninsula and Rhossili's long sandy beach. Rhossili's only pub was miles from anywhere. Out of season it was closed; with a limited amount of alcohol in the car, they were sober as well as happy times.

When did my children's childhood disappear, when did my unwavering commitment to my marriage falter? Sometimes it's impossible to put a time and date to the moment when the present becomes the past. Take Sean's old Ford; it was second-hand when he bought it. How long ago was that – at least ten years, probably more? It served us well. God knows how many miles we travelled in it. Sean's old work horse, as he fondly called it, finally came to rest on the yard in front of the house. As from 4 o'clock this afternoon, when the recovery truck collects it, it too will be a thing of the past, will disappear into yesterday and become nothing but a memory.

I think about the future, wondering what it might hold. The house, the garden, Sean's music, my landscape painting had been part of a shared future. Without Sean a big part of that future has vanished and I'm not sure where to go anymore.

I haven't picked up a brush with the serious intention of finishing a picture since I ran from here. The unfinished paintings I found in the peat shed were so spoiled by damp they went to the tip in Tom's trailer. Not that I wanted to finish them; the daubs of green and indigo, the smears of black and grey, the raging sea and threatening sky was where I put my anger. If only I'd had the sense to talk to Sean, told him about my feelings.

Suddenly, I'm standing at the very end of the beach. I look back – the children are tiny moving figures in the distance. Turning away from the sea, I walk up the beach, sit on the sand and take the shells I collected from my bag. I spread them out in front of me; what pretty things they are. I can name a few – cockle, mussel, limpet, periwinkle – the periwinkle curls like a small black cat enjoying the warmth from the sand. A few of my shells have been tossed by the sea and are as delicate as eggshell, have been bathed in salt water until they became the pearl pink of an early sunrise, the washed out blues of a clear winter sky. Some are as pale as the moon. Very carefully, as if I'm handling a priceless Ming vase, I pick up my prize find. It is very fragile, two perfect dove grey halves held together by a wisp of hinge. Despite the damaging sea, despite the delicate hinge, the two halves have stayed together, weathered the storm as one.

I look down the beach towards the tide mark, wondering what I might find in the accumulation of debris. Tangled amongst the flotsam and jetsam is a length of fisherman's rope, the bright blue adding a splash of colour against the bronze and brown seaweed. I untangle the rope and pull it free. Under it is what children call a "mermaid's purse". I pick it up and gaze out to sea, hoping the little dog fish that hatched from the egg-sac had avoided the jaws of bigger fish and is enjoying life in the ocean.

There is a legend, well known in these parts, about a mermaid who left the sea to come ashore. She cast a spell on a young fisherman who fell in love with her. She stayed with him until a child was born, then she left the baby and the man and went back to the sea, never to be seen again.

I can imagine her diving into the sea with the ease of a cormorant, jumping the waves, swimming away like a porpoise – how I envy her, her lack of guilt for what she had done, her freedom. Thinking about the mermaid, I look at my shells and the fisherman's rope; it's then that I see her, a mermaid created from what the sea has to offer.

I arrive back at the cottage with a bag full of beach finds. I'm so hungry, I throw a sandwich together and take it with me into the outbuildings. After a good rummage around, I find an old picture frame that needs rescuing, a piece of plywood to work on and wire to make an armature. It's the rumble of a heavy goods vehicle coming down the lane that makes me realise how quickly the day has gone by.

The vehicle stops in the yard. I brace myself to go outside. The recovery truck is parked in front of the Ford. The driver jumps from the cab, lets down the ramp and hitches the car to a cable. I watch as it's hauled onto the truck. A part of me wants to shout "Stop" but, like a lot of things that were part of our lives, I must say goodbye.

'I'll get your money,' I call when he finishes securing the car. I give him eighty Euro and watch as he drives away.

The car is already a memory; soon, weeds will colonise the empty space and nobody will know it was ever there. Only I will remember.

I'm so immersed in my thoughts, I don't hear Michael's step. 'I'm sorry,' he says. 'I didn't mean to make you jump. I thought you might want a bit of company.'

'Thank you; I'm glad you came. I know it sounds silly but... saying goodbye... even to an old car... can be hard. It was Sean's car.' I look to where the car had been. 'Without it, the yard looks so terribly empty.'

I turn away and Michael follows me around the house to the garden. I sit on the bench, resting my back against the cottage wall, staring into the distance. Michael sits beside me and says, 'I understand how you feel. Things don't always turn out the way you want. My hopes for the future disappeared a long time ago, when the girl I was engaged to left me.'

He stops speaking and I wonder if he's he waiting for me to say something. But how can I? I'm the leaver, the one who shatters dreams.

He takes a deep breath. 'I don't blame her. It's a hard life being a farmer's wife. She watched her mother, as I watched mine, struggling to raise a family on next to nothing. Washing and scrubbing till her hands were raw, digging in the mud to lift a few potatoes, pulling cabbages to feed us. My father died when I was fifteen. I was the eldest and took over running the farm. My brother and sisters left as soon as they were old enough, but I couldn't leave; how could I – the farm has been in our family for generations. I couldn't let them down.'

He stops speaking. I wait, knowing he has more to say.

'Kathleen, that's her name. She went to London and trained as a nurse. She married and had two children. They're grown up now. I see her brother; he has a farm not far from here. He tells me she's very happy.'

'And what about you; are you happy?'

For a moment he doesn't answer, as though he's choosing his words carefully, then he says, 'I love this land, and the farm. I've struggled to keep it going as my father did and his before him, but what will happen to it after I've gone? I've four nieces and a nephew in America. My brother's son emigrated to Australia. When they were kids they occasionally came for a holiday, but I haven't seen any

~ 284 ~

of them for years. The only time I hear from them is at Christmas; a few words scribbled in Christmas cards. My brother doesn't bother coming anymore, my sister's excuses are it's too far and too expensive. When I die, what will happen? They'll have a hard job selling the place; nobody wants these old cottages. It'll go the same way as thousands of others, left to fall down until it's nothing but a pile of stones.'

'You've nothing to blame yourself for. Your father would have been proud of you; you've a clear conscience and, by the look of you, a good few years left. Anyway, Sean and I bought this house. Some couple will come along and buy yours.'

'But will they be happy? I don't mean to pry, Anna, but you left. You're back now, but for how long. I'm hoping you'll stay.'

CHAPTER 44

My mermaid and the sea green frame were made for each other. When I sat at the kitchen table with glue and paint, the shells and treasures I gathered from the beach fell into place. I carved the mermaid from a piece of drift-wood, coloured her with shades of green and blue, gave her limpet breasts, layered her tail with sea shells. Blue and orange strands of fisherman's rope stream behind her, giving a hair-style any punk would be proud of. The shape of the wood gave two slender arms, a finger pointing at something only she can see, an illusion that any minute she will swim off the living-room wall, never to be seen again.

I cast my eyes around the room, pleased with what I see. Everything is how I want it to be, clean and tidy with a fire laid ready in the wood-burner – even at this time of the year there can be a nip in the air. I give myself a tour of the house; the beds are freshly made, there is a vase of flowers in every room.

I go out into the garden. It's hard to believe that six months ago it was almost back to being the field we'd started with. The hard work has certainly paid off. I've enough veg and salad crop to last well into the autumn, the borders are bright with bedding plants, continual mowing has revived the grass and given a place for the children to play.

I walk down towards a cloud of blue geraniums, splashed with scarlet poppies and marsh marigolds. I hear the meadow pipit's call and see it perched on a branch in the rowan tree, watching me, cocking its head in a way that says, 'I've been expecting you to drop by for a chat.'

'They'll be here soon,' I say. 'Alice rang about an hour ago to let me know they've left Shannon Airport.' I look down at the urn, at Sean's two steel toe-caps partly hidden among the geraniums. 'We're going to be scattering your ashes. I wrote to Diane inviting her to join us but she hasn't replied. She probably wants to get on with her life, forget the whole sorry business. Your dad's not coming. Chris said he hasn't been well since your death and...'

The crunch of wheels on gravel make me lift my head, turn away, saying, 'They're here!'

A people carrier is parked on the drive. The doors open and I don't know who to go to first, then Ella is in front of me. I pick her up, the smell of barley sugar is on her breath, sticky fingers around my neck. Alice is at my side with Stella in her arms. I put Ella down and hold out my hands. Stella hides her face against her mother's shoulder – she's grown. I've missed a whole chunk of her life. Kate puts an arm around me and kisses my cheek. Jenny gives me a hug. Adam calls, 'Anna, how are you?' Sam and James take some luggage from the boot, then they walk towards me with arms full of bags, grins from ear to ear.

The house buzzes with activity. Cases and bags clutter the floor. Jackets are thrown over chairs. Children run in and out of rooms, up and down the stairs.

'Have a look round,' I shout while filling the kettle.

'It looks fantastic, Mum.'

'Where shall we put the cases?'

'Who's sleeping where?'

'Coffee for me, please.'

'Did you make the mermaid? She's beautiful.'

'Can we go outside, Nana?'

'Yes, I'll come with you.'

Children's laughter welcomes the morning. Alice, Adam and the children are in my bedroom – I'm in the small single room, a room full of memories I don't want to face. I hear the children running down the stairs. Alice's quick light tread, her voice saying 'Shh, people are sleeping.'

James shouts, 'It's all right; we're awake.'

Kate calls out from the sitting-room, 'Come in here, girls. I don't get to see my lovely nieces often enough.'

Alice asks, 'Who's for tea?'

'I push the covers aside, calling, 'I'll give you a hand.'

The days fly by too quickly. A week isn't long enough. I'm disappointed and frankly quite jealous that Adam's mum has booked to take Alice and the children to Butlins. Though it wouldn't have made much difference; the rest of my guests have jobs they need to get back to. I think about the picnics on the beach, the games we play in the garden, our walks to the lake and realise how much I'm going to miss them.

We are scattering Sean's ashes today. Bridie, Mary and Tom are with us, and I worry they'll find scattering the ashes in the back garden disrespectful – most people in this part of Ireland bury their dead, in a cemetery, with dignity and a serious manner.

Feeling everyone's eyes on me, I go down to the rowan tree, undo the twine and pick up the urn. As I walk back, I take off the lid, stopping to look at Sean's ashes. I put in my hand, surprised at how coarse and heavy they are. Taking a handful of ash, I throw it to the wind, hoping a little of Sean will be carried out to sea.

I offer the urn to Alice. She takes a handful of ash and scatters it amongst the flowers growing around the rowan tree.

Kate spreads her arms, spins around, leaving a circle of ash on the grass.

Jenny sprinkles hers onto the vegetable patch.

James scatters his amongst the pine trees.

Sam leaves a thin line along the dry stone wall.

Adam disappears around the side of the house – maybe he will lay ash where Sean's old Ford had stood.

Bridie, Mary and Tom stand with their back to the wall. There is a small handful of ash left. I offer them the urn and they shake their heads.

Ella has grown tired of trying to teach Stella how to catch a ball and runs towards me shouting, 'I want to throw granddad's ashes.' She puts her hand into the urn, throws the ash into the air. One minute she's laughing, the next she's running to her mother crying, 'Granddad's in my eyes.' Kate and I look at each other and smile as I ask myself what the neighbours must think.

Mary and Tom don't stay long. After a cup of tea and a slice of cake, they give their apologies and go home to feed the cattle. Bridie says she's tired; I suspect she's wants to sit in her armchair and watch the three tenors.

Later that evening, when the children are in bed, we sit at the kitchen table finishing the quiche, sharing the last of the wine.

'I thought I was going to feel sad,' says Kate. 'But it wasn't like that. I felt we were doing what Dad would have wanted.'

'Yes,' nods Alice. 'I'm sure he was with us. Was your little bird in the garden, Mum?'

'He might have been. I'm usually on my own when I see him.'

'Do you get many visitors?' asks Sam.

'Bridie calls in, but I mainly go to her. Mary's busy but I know her and Tom are there if I need them. Michael calls if he's passing.'

'Who's Michael?' asks Kate.

'He helps me with the heavy work. He finished jobs that Sean started. He laid the gravel for me.'

'I can imagine it being quite lonely. You're very isolated,' says Jenny.

'Adam and I found it depressing,' says Alice.

I look at her. 'That's because it was difficult for you, and I'm sorry. I'm sure if I'd been here you'd have a different impression.'

'I don't think so; I missed the city when we were living here.'

'Do you think you'll move back to England?'

'Sorry,' I say when I hear Jenny's voice. 'I was miles away.'

'Do you think you'll stay here, or will you go back to England?'

'I don't know. I need to think about it. Liz, Sue and Vicky are coming over in October. They'll want to know what I'm going to be doing with myself, but I won't make any big decisions.'

As soon as they start carrying the luggage to the car, I've made up my mind. Before I know it, I'm saying, 'Why don't you come here for Christmas? We'll have a real old-fashioned one: log fires, walks in the country. Bridie's sister keeps geese; I'll order one. I'll cut down one of the pine trees and the children can decorate it.'

They stop what they're doing. 'I haven't thought about Christmas,' says Alice. She looks at Adam. 'I suppose we can give your mother a miss for one year.'

'Yes, why not. They'll be seeing Lydia, so they won't be on their own.'

'I don't know,' says Kate. 'It can be difficult getting time off at Christmas, and you know what we're like – if we're not working, we'll be partying.'

'What do you think about spending Christmas here with Nana?' says Adam to the children.

'Yes,' screams Ella. 'Nana has a huge big chimney. Santa can bring lots of presents.'

'Me too,' shouts Stella.

'We'd love to join you,' says Jenny, 'but we always visit James' mum on Christmas Day. Every year we think it will be her last. She's ninety, so you never know, we might be with you.'

I watch them climb into the car, wait until they disappear from sight. I truly believe that extreme emotion can change an atmosphere, that joy, fear, happiness, sadness, can leave its mark. For the past few years I've been weighed down with sorrow and self-pity. I left some of those emotions in this house, they are still here now. I want to dispel those negative feelings, to send them packing to the tune of love, laughter and Christmas bells.

CHAPTER 45

I open the door, go out to a blanket of mist as grey as the ash I'm carrying; a chill is on my skin and the smell of the Atlantic.

I empty the ash under the hedge and hurry inside, wondering if my guests are still sleeping. There was no sound from them when I came downstairs; even the rasp of metal on metal when I raked the stove didn't wake them.

Liz, Sue and Vicky flew into Shannon yesterday. When I picked them up I asked if they'd like to take a look at Ennis – in the two hours we were there they bought more clothes than I have in six months. After cramming their purchases in with the luggage, we drove to the beach and had a walk on the sand. By the time we arrived at the house, it was beginning to get dark.

The next few hours were taken up with having a quick tour of the house, explaining how I made the mermaid, eating cottage pie, deciding what to wear, and waiting to use the bathroom. It was well gone nine when the four of us stood at the window, willing the taxi to arrive.

I'd been worried the music would bring me another bout of sadness; they assured me that having my old mates at my side things would be different. I wanted them to enjoy their stay so I recommended we went to Blondie's.

Blondie's, as usual, was packed. What with half a dozen musicians keeping the music going and the blarney coming from three old men in flat caps sat at our table, we were unable to do much talking.

It must have been a good few hours after midnight when the taxi drove away, when the four of us looked up into a beautiful star-studded sky and spun around and around till our necks ached. Giddy from star gazing, we fell into the house. I can't remember much after that, but I do know I enjoyed myself.

I've just about finished lighting the stove when Vicky comes into the kitchen, flops into a chair, saying, 'What the hell did they put in that Guinness? We didn't have that much to drink! What time did we get back?'

'I don't know. Pubs close when they want to here. Would you like tea or coffee?'

Liz's voice comes loud and clear from the back bedroom. 'Did someone say coffee?'

'Yes,' I shout. 'I'll bring you one.'

The living-room door opens and Sue emerges, a vision in pink from rollers and hairnet to dressing-gown and fluffy slippers. 'Morning,' she says, rushing towards the bathroom. 'I'll have coffee but I must have a pee first.'

It's gone twelve and we're still wearing our night clothes. There's been so much to talk about we haven't noticed the small hand making its journey around the clock face. The coffee pot has been refilled a number of times. Toast crumbs, sticky knives and the open pot of marmalade remind me that breakfast was a while ago and yet we carry on talking.

'So that's the story,' says Vicky. 'The day centre has a reprieve. Clients will keep their places for the moment but there won't be any more referrals, numbers will decline and they'll shut us down.'

'It's not all bad news,' says Sue. 'Have you told Anna about your new man?'

'You told me you've met someone. Is it serious?'

'Yes, very. Jim's lovely.' She looks at Sue for confirmation.

'He is. I like him. He's the complete opposite of Craig.'

'I agree,' says Liz, 'and he's better looking.'

'Lily approves as well. As soon as Jim comes into the house she's whining around his legs, telling him to sit down so she can jump on his lap.'

'She always did like men. She loved Sean.' I look at Liz. 'What happened to that man you brought to the party? What was his name?'

'Ian. He started going on about us living together. When I told him I didn't want to he said our relationship was going nowhere. I thought it was okay. Anyway, we fell out. It's a shame; I liked him. Trouble is they change as soon as you start living with them.'

Sue starts unwinding the curlers from her hair, putting them in a neat pile away from the crumbs. She says, 'I agree with Liz. I haven't bothered with them since Derrick and I divorced. Once bitten twice shy.'

'Jim's different. In fact,' says Vicky looking towards me, 'since we're on the subject, I was wondering if it would be alright if he moves in with me. We...'

'Don't you think it's a bit early to be thinking of living together?' interrupts Liz.

Vicky shoots her a look that means mind your own business. 'What I want to say is we'd like to give it a try. See how we get on. Jim lives in a bedsit. His marriage broke up about two years ago. Like me, he has some money from the sale of his house. If we put it together we'd have a sizeable deposit to buy a place of our own. We're both cautious; we've had bad experiences. Of course, we'll pay extra rent. If you want a reference, ask Blodwyn – she thinks he's lush!'

I look at her and smile. 'If Blodwyn thinks he's lush who am I to argue? As long as I still have the use of my room he can stay as long as he likes. Don't worry about paying extra rent.

'Thank you, Anna, that's very generous of you. Jim's going to be so pleased. Will you be back for Christmas?'

'No. Alice and the family are coming here for Christmas. I'm really looking forward to it. It will be the kind of Christmas I've always dreamed of: a log fire, walks on the beach while the goose is roasting.' – I'd wanted to say a peaceful Christmas, had stopped myself when I thought about what it implied, that they may think I was looking forward to a Christmas without Sean, when the truth is I would give anything to have him with me, sober or drunk. 'It will probably be the last Christmas I spend here. I'm going to put the house on the market.' I stop speaking for a moment, wondering how to explain. 'You see... when Sean and I were here life was very difficult. We were both unhappy... The sadness is still here, as though the walls are made of sponge that has soaked those unhappy times down to its foundations. Running off, throwing myself at... the way I did was a terrible thing to do. When I think about the things I said, how I treated Sean, I feel ashamed. Every part of this house holds a picture I want to forget.'

Liz touches my hand. 'Anna, you mustn't keep...'

'I'm all right,' I say, sitting up straight. 'It's just that I want to leave this house on a happy note.'

'Will you move back to Bristol?' she asks.

'No, I want to go to Ilfracombe. It's a small harbour town in North Devon, not far from Woolacombe. I'll never forget getting back from that holiday and finding Kate waiting for me. All along I'd had a feeling something was wrong.'

'Why Ilfracombe?'

'Before we had Alice, Sean and I had a holiday there.' I hold out my hand. 'He bought me this ring. There was this funny little jewellery shop by the harbour. We stayed in a flat above a post office. We couldn't keep our hands off each other. We made love day and night. One morning, I managed to get him to go for a walk. A huge wave got Sean soaked. We were both laughing. It was so funny and...'

'Anna, you won't find him there,' says Liz, her voice full of concern.

'What do you mean?'

'Sean! You won't find him there. He's gone. He's dead. You must stop searching.'

Suddenly Vicky points to the window. 'Look! The mist has cleared.'

'I told you,' I say, leaping up, glad to escape the questioning look in Liz's eyes. 'These mists disappear as quickly as they come. See, there's a patch of blue. I want to show you the Burren. There's a fantastic drive along the coast road to Fanore. The beach has the whitest sand I've ever seen. Let's get ready. We can clear the table when we get back.'

It hardly seems five minutes ago when I was driving to the airport to pick them up and now we're saying goodbye. I watch them walk away – Sue tottering on her high heels, Liz's jet-black hair, Vicky's swinging ponytail. There was no more mention of Sean. Their instincts told them to stay away from his name. They don't understand that I need to find out why I left; if and when we stopped loving each other. We were happy once. I know we were. The holiday in Ilfracombe is clear in my mind. I remember waking up to of the sound of seagulls, watching Sean sleeping, my heart so full of love I felt it could burst. I thought the sound of the gulls, the smell of the sea, Sean by my side was enough, all I would ever need.

CHAPTER 46

I've been walking up and down these lanes looking for holly for what seems like hours, but I haven't seen a single twig of it. I don't want much, a couple of sprigs will do.

Trees and shrubs have a tough time in this climate. Those that do survive look as though the devil himself is behind them, their gnarled branches reaching like fingers to escape the battering wind that bends them double. Still, I've pulled plenty of ivy from stone walls and I have a carrier bag full to the brim with pine cones so, giving up on the holly, I turn and head for home.

It's one of those rare winter days when the wind doesn't blow, when the land holds its breath beneath a blanket of moist air. Smoke rises from isolated dwellings, grey snakes in a grey sky. A car speeds past and disappears over the brow of the hill. A dog strains at its chains, its bark lost in the distance as I hurry home.

I reach the top of the lane and look down at the house. It nestles amongst the outbuildings, has rooted itself to the slope of the hill. How long has it been there? I can only guess – two, three hundred years? What dramas has it witnessed? During the potato famine, did its people starve? Clare was a stronghold for the IRA at the time of the uprising; was anyone involved who'd lived here? How many people have been born, have died within its walls?

When was the last time that greenery was carried through the door to make a Christmas wreath, when presents were hidden in the attic, when the smell of cinnamon and nutmeg wafted through the rooms, cakes iced and crackers pulled?

I go into the house, shake the ivy and cones out of the bags onto the table, then go out to the garden for a few sprigs of fir. Whenever I'm in the garden I listen for the pipit's call, hoping to see a small movement, a flutter of wings from what I'd come to think of as my bird. I don't know what has happened to it; as far as I know pipits don't migrate. The last time I saw my pipit was a few days before we scattered Sean's ashes. Perhaps it overheard me saying I'm planning to sell the house. I laugh at myself, thinking – don't be an idiot; he probably fancied a change of address or was unlucky enough to be caught by a cat.

I break off a couple of fir sprigs then go over to a small neatly shaped tree. I've had my eye on it since I knew Alice and the family were spending Christmas with me. The children will enjoy watching it being felled, helping to bring it into the house and decorating it.

Leaving the tree, I wander over to the vegetable patch. An untidy line of Brussels wear their sprouts like medals, some of the cabbage leaves have been nibbled to lace, an abundance of swedes and parsnips are ready to be lifted.

Wondering if the people who buy this house will enjoy the garden as much as I do, I turn away and go into the house. I switch on the radio; carols are being sung. Singing along with them, I sit at the table, threading ivy through a willow wreath. The radio and I are halfway through "Oh Little Town of Bethlehem" when there's a knock on the door. Expecting it to be Mary calling in for the vegetables I promised, I stand up and answer it.

I'm not surprised to see Michael – he's a regular visitor – or to hear him say, 'I've been working with Tom and thought you might need a bit of company.' I'm about to reply when he pulls a branch of mistletoe from behind his back, holds it over my head and puts his arm around me.

It feels good to be held, would be easy to return his kiss; instead I pull away. Laughing to hide my fluster, I ask, 'Where did you get the mistletoe?' I sweep a few stray ivy leaves into my hand and put them into the bin. He moves towards me, saying, 'They've opened a new restaurant in Lahinch. I know you're busy, what with the family coming, but after they go back... after the New Year, would you like to come out for a meal with me?'

I pick up a tea towel, wipe my hands, wondering, if it had been another time, if Sean wasn't forever in my thoughts, if I wasn't missing my family the way I do, would I have answered yes?

'I'm sorry, but no. I've decided to sell the house. I'm going back to England. I don't want to make things more complicated than they are.'

Disappointment is in his eyes. He shrugs his shoulders, gives a small smile and says, 'All the nice girls go to England. But I can still take you out for a meal, can't I?'

'If you don't mind, I think it would be better if we didn't.' I take my eyes from his, not wanting him to recognise a mutual attraction between us. I pick up the kettle. 'Would you like a drink?'

'No, I must get back to Tom.'

'I hear you're spending Christmas Day with them. Don't tell them I'm selling the house, or Bridie; I haven't said anything and I'd rather tell them myself.'

He goes to the door, turns to look at me, saying, 'Of course not. Have a good Christmas.'

I don't think Michael will drop by again. I'll miss him.

Can anything be perfect? When I wake on Boxing Day morning with dreamy half-awake eyes, it seems almost possible. I rest my head against the back of the sofa and look around me. The children's presents, their books, the games and puzzles are neatly stacked on the sideboard. Chestnut shells litter the hearth, a sliver of morning light comes through the crack in the curtains, giving a sparkle to the decorations on the tree. The room is picture perfect, recapitulates a happy family Christmas Day. My eyes fall on the untouched bottles of wine, the whiskey opened but not empty, the bottle of Baileys, still half full, and I remember other Christmases, other times.

I don't want to harp back, don't want to cast my mind to past Christmases, but I can't help myself. There are too many to remember in detail, but they all had one thing in common – every bottle empty by nightfall, waking to a Boxing Day morning with a discontent, a despair that grew with each New Year – I don't want to be disloyal when I say yesterday was so nearly perfect because you weren't with us...

Bridie gave me the Baileys – this year, I didn't have to hide it. Tom and Mary knocked on the door on Christmas Eve – I invited them in without having to invent an excuse; didn't have to send them away because I was ashamed to let them see you sprawled across the table or unconscious on the floor.

This morning, we're going to the beach. There's going to be a Boxing Day swim, a collection for charity. Adam might take the plunge. This afternoon, if the weather holds, the children will fly their kites.

Can you hear Stella's voice? She's in the little front bedroom, shouting at Ella to wake up. Any moment the door to this room will open and they will appear. They'll climb in beside me and another nearly perfect day will begin.

CHAPTER 47

For a few moments I look up at what had been Sean's bedroom window, remembering the dramas played there and the night he died, then I push open the gate and step onto the garden path. I stand at the door wondering if I should use my key or ring the bell – Vicky and I agreed to share the house, but Jim is living here now. I give the door a light tap. A man's stocky figure appears behind the obscured glass and the door opens, revealing a round friendly face and a pleasant smile.

'You must be Jim,' I say, holding out my hand.

'You must be Anna! Come in.' Then he goes to the stairs and shouts, 'Vicky! It's Anna.'

I leave my case in the hall and follow him into the kitchen. 'Vicky will be down in a minute,' he says. 'Let me take your coat. Make yourself comfortable. What would you like to drink?' Still talking, he fills the kettle. 'Did you have a good journey? I've only been to Ireland once. A group of us went to Dublin for a stag night. I can't remember much about it.'

The sound of steps running down the stairs makes me stand up from the table. 'I'm sorry I'm early,' I say as Vicky throws her arm around me. 'I was hoping Kate and I would have time for a coffee at the airport but she had to get to a dental appointment.'

'The earlier the better,' she says.

I go back to the table. Vicky sits beside me saying, 'I hope Jim hasn't been chatting your head off. He always talks a lot when he's nervous. He was worried you wouldn't like him and he'd have to leave.'

'Vicky! What have you been saying about me?' I laugh.

Jim gives me a grin. 'Only that you're the landlady and if I don't keep this house immaculate and love Lily into the bargain, you'll tell me to leave. Shall I make a pot of tea? By the way, I have to wait on her and Lily, hand, foot and finger.'

'Get on with you,' she says in a flirty voice. 'Go and make that tea. Anna must be famished.' She turns to me, saying, 'Would you like something to eat?'

I shake my head. 'Not at the moment. Where is Lily?'

'There.' She points to the radiator. 'Jim bought her that sheepskin pouch. She loves it. Whether the heating's on or not she's curled up like a pea in a pod.'

Jim puts the teapot onto the table, saying, 'It was a bit of a ploy. Vicky and Lily were both trying to get on my lap. I had to do something to get one of them off me.'

Vicky gives a light tap on his cheek. 'Excuse him,' she says. 'He's like this day and night.'

And hasn't it done you good, I think. The happiness on your face says it all.

Jim passes me a mug of tea. I take a sip before saying, 'I would have come over before, but I've been reluctant to leave the house. If I don't light the fires every day it gets so damp; anyone interested in buying the place will turn around and walk straight out. Of course, I've had to make an exception; being with the girls for the anniversary of Sean's death is really important to me.'

'I can't believe he's been gone a year,' says Vicky.

'Nor can I. Anyway, I've decided not to worry about the house. Nobody's viewed it yet. The estate agent said people don't start looking till the spring. I hope I sell the house this year. I hate being away from everyone.'

'Are you still thinking of buying in Ilfracombe?'

'Yes. I love being near the sea and Ilfracombe's only a couple of hours' drive to Bristol. People can visit me without all the expense of planes or ferries, plus there's a train station in Barnstaple, which isn't far from Ilfracombe.'

'What are you planning to do tomorrow?'

'Ella will be in school and Stella's in nursery. Kate's got a bit of time off so we're meeting up at Alice's; we'll decide what we're doing then.'

I finish drinking my tea, go over to Lily and stroke her head. 'Thank you for looking after her so well. If you don't mind, I'll go to my room and unpack.'

'I'll bring your case up,' says Jim.

Leaving Lily, I say, 'Thanks, Jim, but I can manage; it's not heavy.'

'Food will be ready in about an hour,' says Vicky.

I reach the top of the stairs, stop as I look through the open door of what had been Sean's room. His single bed has been replaced with a double but to me it is still Sean's room, as though every moment I'd spent there with him is trapped between the floor and ceiling. I go into my own bedroom, remembering the last Christmas, the comfort I felt when Sean came into my bed, the feel of his arm around me, the loss when he moved away and I heard the pad of his footsteps on the floorboards. You would think Vicky and Jim's happiness would expel these images, but they're still here, as vivid and alive as they ever were.

I didn't expect Sean's death day to be a bright and sunny one, or that we'd be smiling as we sit looking through the pile of photographs in front of us.

'Look at this one,' says Kate, passing me a photograph creased with age. 'Do you remember when we managed to get Dad to roll up his trousers and go into the sea for a paddle? When he saw you taking the photo he tried to grab the camera. Where were we?'

'The Gower,' I say looking at Sean's laughing face.

My phone rings and I put the photograph down. Leaving the kitchen, I put the phone to my ear.

'Anna, its Rasheen.'

'Rasheen?'

'Yes, from "Open Doors".'

'Oh, sorry, I didn't recognise your voice.'

'We've sold your house.'

'You've what?'

'Sold your house.'

Her words don't make sense. 'When?'

'Yesterday. A couple called the office. I met them at your house and they fell in love with it.'

'But I only left yesterday.'

'It was in the afternoon. They've offered the asking price. Are you all right? It's what you wanted, isn't it?'

I'm close to tears and I can't understand why. 'Yes, it's just I wasn't prepared. I didn't expect it to go so quickly.'

'Well, it's a lovely house. When are you back in Ireland?'

'The end of next week.'

'Well, come in when you're ready. Do you have a solicitor?'

'Yes, Sean Casey.'

'Okay. Enjoy the rest of your stay. I look forward to hearing from you soon.'

Still in a daze, I go back to the girls. Their smiles changing to concern as they put the photographs they're holding onto the table. 'What's the matter?' asks Alice.

'That was the estate agent. They've sold the house.'

'That was quick.'

'Yes, brilliant, so why are you upset?'

'I don't know. It's probably an accumulation of things. We had so many hopes and dreams. I thought I might have been able to carry on living there. That I could have made the house as Sean would have wanted it. When she said "we've sold your house" those dreams vanished. I feel as though I've let him down and now I'm crying for nothing and everything.'

'Come on, Mum,' says Kate, standing up and putting her arm around me. 'Go and wash your face, put a bit of make-up on. Dad wouldn't like to see you upset; not on his death day. Let's go out for lunch. We'll drink red wine in his memory.'

We choose a restaurant down by the city docks, a table near the window to watch the world go by. 'I've got another three days' leave,' says Kate. 'Why don't we drive down to Ilfracombe? We could stay a couple of nights and have a look at what houses are on the market.'

'Are you sure? Can you spare the time?'

'Yes, it'll be fun. What about you, Alice? Can you get Adam to look after the kids for a few days?'

'He's really busy, but I think you two should go. You might as well make the most of your time while you're here, Mum.'

I can't remember the route Sean and I took when we came to Ilfracombe. Kate wants to come the picturesque way, so we leave the A361 and make our way along a winding road that takes us past thatched and slate roof cottages, wooded valleys and pasture land. We drive slowly through the coastal village of Combe Martin, pick up speed as we hurry past deserted caravan parks and campsites.

A sign welcomes us to Ilfracombe. The buildings are grander here, a mixture of large Victorian villas and elegant Georgian terraces. I recognise the post office and say, 'That's where your dad and I stayed!' Looking back, I watch it disappear from view.

We turn onto the High Street, to an eclectic mix of shops, restaurants and pubs.

'Wilder Road should be right at the traffic lights,' says Kate. 'The hotel is opposite the beach.'

At first glance, the hotel is impressive. The turrets, balconies and balustrades wouldn't look out of place in Italy. And then we notice the mismatched net curtains hanging at the windows, the frayed edges on the blue patterned carpet in reception, the old-fashioned, red, embossed wallpaper.

The receptionist – a fifty something woman with red lipstick bleeding patterns into the fine lines around her mouth – flashes purple nail-varnish and hands me a key, saying, 'Room Nine. First on the right at the landing.'

We climb the stairs trying to stifle our giggles. 'I wonder what the room's like,' whispers Kate.

I push the curtain aside. The saving grace is the view. Huge waves crash onto the rocks then roll up the beach accompanied by swirling foam and the flight of gulls.

On the far side of the beach is a stone wall, a flight of steps and a path. 'You see that path,' I say, 'your Dad and I were walking along it when a massive wave came over the wall. Sean was drenched. We had to go back so he could change. It was so funny we couldn't stop laughing.'

Across from the path is a steep piece of land; at the very top is a flag and what might be a figure. Pointing, I say, 'What do you think that is?'

'I don't know. It looks like a statue.'

'I can't remember a statue being there.'

Kate looks at her watch, saying, 'Time's getting on. I noticed a couple of estate agents on the High Street. I think we should have a look.'

'What sort of property are you looking for?' asks the young woman behind the desk.

'A house with three or four bedrooms and a small garden.'

'We've a few that might suit you.' She leaves the desk and goes to a cabinet; opens a drawer and sorts through the files.

'Have a look at these. If there's anything that interests you let us know. Oh, I'd better give you a map.'

We go outside. I look across the road, saying, 'There's a café. Let's go and have a cup of tea and a look at these details.'

The cafe, like the town, is almost deserted. I go to the counter. 'It's very quiet,' I say to the assistant as she makes a pot of tea.

'It always is this time of year,' she says, filling a silver tray with cups and saucers, milk, sugar and a teapot. 'You should see it in the summer. You get all types here then. We get rushed off our feet.'

I take the tray to where Kate is sat. 'Anything interesting?' I ask.

'A few; I particularly like this one.'

I sit down and take the details from her. The house is a modern three-bedroomed semi with parking for one car. It has gas central heating and everything anyone could want for comfortable living.

'What do you think?'

'I'm not sure,' I say, picking up the rest of the details and looking through them. One catches my eye and I pass it to Kate.

'Why do you need five bedrooms? There's no parking and you know what these old Victorian houses are like. They cost a fortune to heat and there's always something going wrong with them. You'd be better off with something modern.'

'I suppose you're right.'

'There's these as well,' says Kate, passing more details to me. 'Perhaps, while they're still open, we should go back to the estate agent and arrange some viewings.'

'Well, did you like any of them?' asks Kate with a hint of exasperation in her voice.

'They're okay,' I say, while thinking how boring they are, with their featureless rooms, compact kitchens and paved drives. 'But I would prefer something closer to the High Street and the beach.'

'Trouble with that, Mum, unless you get a flat, you're going to end up with a big house you don't need. Then there's the upkeep and no parking, which will always be a problem, especially in the summer when the holidaymakers are here.'

'I know you're right, Kate, but I really want to view the house in Glen Road. I can't make any decisions until I've looked at it.'

She takes a deep breath. 'Okay, we'll go back to the agent.'

'It's a short walk from here,' says the agent as she gets her coat.

We follow her out of the office, across the road, past the café and onto a side turning that takes us onto Glen Road.

At the top of Glen Road is a pet shop; next to the pet shop is a chapel. Above the chapel door, large blue lettering proclaims "CHRISTIAN SPIRITUAL CHURCH"; an information board has times of openings and services.

Kate and the estate agent are waiting outside a terraced house. I hurry down the road to join them.

The garden is smaller than I would have liked it to be – I tell myself that spending most of my time gardening is not what I want anymore. A climbing plant frames the door, another makes its way around the bay window; an abundance of daffodils are beginning to show their heads. 'It's pretty, isn't it,' says the agent as she opens the gate.

As soon as I go through the door I know I am going to like the house. It reminds me of our house in Bristol, the high ceilings and large sash windows, the varnished floorboards; the feeling of space Sean and I loved so much. 'I want it,' I tell the agent.

'Mum! You can't. I thought you wanted a garden.'

'I can put some pots in the back yard and the front is pretty.'

'But you need to look around; there might be something else.'

'I want this one.'

She looks at the estate agent. 'Perhaps we can look at the house again tomorrow.'

'Of course, come back to the office and I'll look in my diary. It's a lovely house, Mrs Curtin. It's only just come on the market. It won't be long before it's snapped up.'

Bracing ourselves against the wind, Kate and I follow the path around what we now know is Capstone. I see Sean's laughing face on the spot where he was soaked by the wave and look at Kate, saying, 'Your dad and I climbed to the top of Capstone; would you like to?' She nods and follows me up the zigzag path.

Kate is quiet, annoyed because I'm going to buy the house in Glen Road, but her moods don't last long; they disappear as quickly as they come.

As we climb higher a statue comes into view. When we reach the top we see the bronze statue of a young girl. She is standing on tiptoe, her hair and clothes caught in the wind, her arm held wide, ready to fly. A plaque reads "Ekaterene (Kate) Frolov. Born Moscow 23.12.1986. A beautiful girl, full of life and energy, who tragically fell to her death from Hillsborough, 19 July 2000. Kate, you are always with us."

2000 – the year Sean and I moved to Ireland. Sean and I were starting a new life and her family were grieving. I think to myself, could there be anything worse than losing a child.

I look at my Kate and put my arm around her. She smiles. I realise how lucky I am and the future starts to look much brighter.

CHAPTER 48

From the moment the loaded removal van rattled its way up the lane, I've been pacing each room, listening to the echo of my feet on the floor, imprinting every nook and cranny into my mind in case I forget.

My feelings have taken me by surprise. You would think after weeks of packing and cleaning, of driving back and forth to the tip and charity shops, I'd want nothing more than to leave this house, go to Mary's and collapse in a chair.

Picking up my coat and bag, I go outside and put them into the car. Then I stand for a moment, looking at the outbuildings, watching the house martins going to and fro, envying their freedom to visit next year.

I take one last walk, one last message to the rowan tree, saying, 'The dream of living here was for the two of us. I thought I could live your share but I can't. I miss our daughters, our granddaughters. I'm closer to you when I'm with them.'

I cast my eye around the garden, breathing in the scent of blackthorn blossom, listening to the sound of bird song, telling myself that nothing stays the same, people and things come and go. The pipit left the garden. Sean's ashes will have followed, been taken by the wind, blown across land and sea. A few may have fallen onto Ilfracombe.

I turn around, go back to the house, take the key from my pocket and lock the door. I won't enter this house again. I might stop and stare at it from the road, but I won't knock on the door. They might invite me in and I will be the stranger.

I open the car door, sit in the driving seat, looking across the field to Mary's bungalow wondering what I would have done without her and Bridie's help.

I turn on the ignition, drive out of the yard onto the lane. Steering the Cinquecento around the potholes, I say, 'Well, old friend, I'm sure Mary will find you a good owner, but now you and I must part company.'

CHAPTER 49

'Morning, Mum; is it ok if Lydia comes down with us next weekend? Give us a call when you get this message.'

'Alice! Of course she can. I haven't seen Lydia for ages. She's expecting a baby, isn't she?'

'Yes, it's due in November. Do you remember her little girl, Tamsin?'

'Yes, it was a long time ago. Stella was crawling at the time and Tamsin had just started walking.'

'Tamsin's a few months older than Stella. The weather's supposed to be good and I thought it would be nice if they could spend some time on the beach together. I'll bring their costumes; Ella wants to show you how well she swims. Lydia can be a bit of a worrier, but I told her the pool at Tunnels Beach is safe, and it's easy to keep an eye on the children.'

'Is Adam coming with you?'

'No. He'd rather we were out of the way. He wants to make a start on decorating the lounge...'

I put the phone down, thinking how much life has changed for me; that coming to Ilfracombe was the right thing to do. I'm not short of guests. I'd only been here a week when Sue and Liz arrived – we had a wild time sampling Ilfracombe pubs. It took us all Sunday to get over it.

Kate and Sam spent the whole of their annual leave here. You name it, we did it: walking the coast path, swimming, going to the theatre, eating out. Kate now loves the house, but I knew she would.

Vicky and Jim were the last to leave. They want to carry on renting the house for a while and asked if they could put a few things in the attic. I told them they could, that the only thing up there is a small brown suitcase. They're still hoping to buy a place of their own and wondered if Lily could go with them. They were surprised when I said yes. I had to explain that having the freedom to go to Bristol and visit my family whenever I want is a priority; that I'd been worried about Lily as taking her to Bristol or putting her in kennels would be very traumatic for her. It didn't take long to convince them; when they left my house, it was with big smile.

After Alice and her crew leave, Jenny and James will be here. Even Blodwyn is considering abandoning Trev for a few days to visit me. I don't think Bill will be coming for a while. Chris says that, since Sean died, Bill hasn't wanted to go anywhere and has become a bit of a recluse.

I love this town – the friendliness of the people, the architecture, the glorious scenery. On clear days, I can look across the sea to the Gower Peninsula, remembering the happy family weekends we spent there. A walk around Capstone brings Sean's laughing face as the wave washes over him. The little jewellery shop by the harbour is now an ice-cream kiosk, but if I stand with my back to it I can conjure the moment when Sean put the ring on my finger. The post office is unchanged; the door to the flat exactly as it was. Whenever I'm there I look back through the years and know, without a doubt, there was a time when we I loved each other.

It's late when Alice, Lydia and the children arrive at my house. I help get the children ready for bed, leave them while their mothers read the final bedtime stories.

It's not long before Alice and Lydia join me in the sitting-room. Alice flops into an armchair and pours herself a glass of wine. I give Lydia the tonic water she requested, and she stretches out on the sofa, saying, 'The nice thing about being pregnant is being waited on. It's about the only time Mark fusses over me, and I love it.'

'Me too,' says Alice. 'Not that I'm planning to get pregnant. Two's enough. Not that we can moan about our men.'

'No,' says Lydia, 'though Adam was a right pain when we were kids.'

'What was Dad like when you were pregnant, Mum?'

Always keen to talk about Sean, I put my glass onto the coffee table, saying, 'Kindness itself. He looked forward to being a dad. He adored you girls.' I stop speaking for a moment. 'Then things started to change. Our sex life dwindled to nothing and we drifted apart. I blamed his drinking but the blame was obviously mine. He and Diane had an active sex life! She cared about her appearance. I never bothered with what I looked like. Why didn't I take an interest in his music? Been cheerful, not the miserable person I became. Who would want a partner like that?'

The girls twiddle with the stems of their glasses. They didn't drive a hundred miles to listen to me talking about my sex life. Trying to lighten the mood, I put on a jovial voice, asking, 'What do you think of the house?'

'It's lovely,' pipes up Lydia with a touch of relief.

'I'm pleased with it. It's so handy for everything – the beach, the shops; we've a cinema and a theatre.'

'And a spiritualist church,' adds Alice.

Lydia looks at me, saying, 'Have you, have you been there yet?'

'No. I'm a bit of a sceptic.'

'I'd love to go. Will you come with me Alice?'

'Yes. I'm curious myself. Would you mind babysitting, Mum?'

'No. You go. They've a notice board with times of services on the wall.'

We leave the beach in plenty of time to feed the children and get them into bed. I've promised Ella she can stay up until Alice and Lydia get back from the service. I'm looking through the Radio Times for a programme that Ella and I can watch together, when Alice, carrying Stella, walks into the room. 'Stella's been sick,' she says. 'It's probably one ice-cream too many.'

I put the Radio Times down. 'How is she now?'

'A bit tearful.'

Lydia pokes her head around the door. 'Is she okay?'

'Yes, but I won't go out. I don't want to leave her. Is Tamsin all right?'

'Yes, I'm about to put her to bed.'

Ella comes into the room, asking in a worried voice, 'Has Stella stopped being sick?'

'Yes,' says Alice. 'There's nothing to worry about. She's fine now.' She looks at Lydia. 'I'm sorry to let you down.' She turns to me, saying, 'Will you go with her, Mum?'

I think about it for a moment. 'Yes, why not.'

The interior of the Chapel is not what I expected. From the outside, apart from the large blue lettering, it looks like a very old Victorian building. The inside is another story.

A plush, royal blue carpet covers the floor. Twenty or so people – mostly women – sit waiting on lines of chairs upholstered in a shiny, bright blue material. A central aisle leads to a rostrum; on the table in front of it there is a brass cross and a vase of marguerites and blue delphiniums. A smartly dressed elderly man wearing a navy suit, dark tie and a pale blue shirt is sat conversing with a middle-aged woman. Her spiked platinum blonde hair, piercings, and the array of tattoos covering her arms make her look out of place amongst the plainly dressed audience.

Lydia taps my arm and I take my eyes away from the woman. 'Let's sit at the back,' she says. I follow her; we pick up a sheet of music and sit down.

The elderly man stands up from the rostrum, gives a little cough and says, 'Ladies and gentlemen, I'd like to introduce our guest for the evening.' He indicates the woman. 'Tamara Smith from Plymouth. She's a respected medium, both here in Devon and other parts of the UK. I'm sure she'll have messages of love for you from your loved ones on the other side. Let us welcome her.'

The congregation gives a round of applause; he waits for it to fade then says, 'But first we will sing our opening song. The words are on your sheet of music.'

There is a shuffling of feet as everyone stands, then the tinny sound of a cassette playing Gerry and the Pacemakers' version of "You'll Never Walk Alone".

I'm sure most of us mouth the words. Only Gerry hits the high note at the end of the song. Everyone except Tamara sits down. All eyes are now on her.

She casts her eyes over the waiting faces then points into the congregation, saying, 'Can I come to the lady wearing the red jumper... Yes you, love. I've been given the name of George. He passed to the other side two years ago. Do you accept the name of George?... Thank you. He says, when the autumn comes, don't forget to prune the roses. Last year you forgot and this summer they aren't at their best. God bless you.'

She looks around the room again. 'I'd like to come to the lady with the long blonde hair... Yes you, dear. I'm receiving a Nora. She was your aunt, a favourite aunt. Do you accept Nora?... Thank you. The little silver brooch with the opal was meant for you. It's on a coat in your mother's wardrobe. Your mother will understand that Nora wants you to have something to remember her by. God bless you.'

~ 316 ~

Tamara is looking our way, points towards us, saying, 'The lady in the back row.' Lydia and I glance at each other. 'The lady next to the aisle,' says Tamara, and I look at her. 'Yes you, love. A man followed you in. A man in the spirit world. He's standing next to you. He's slim with dark hair. He's wearing steel toe cap boots. He's showing me his hands. He was a builder. Do you know a man in the spirit world who fits this description?'

Ignoring my tears, I nod.

'Thank you. He says there were angry words before he died, that you have been very distressed. His leaving left you with a sorrow you're finding hard to bear.'

I am holding Lydia's hand, willing Tamara to tell me more.

Tamara touches the back of her chair. 'I'm feeling giddy, as though I'm about to fall.' She moves away from the chair, stares at the floor, mutters something, nods, then says, 'He's a shy man. There are things he wants to say to you in private. He would like to communicate when the service is over. Will you see me then?'

I don't know who else she speaks to, or what is said. I'm oblivious to anything other than my need to hear what Tamara has to tell me. Lydia's voice saying she will see me back at the house wakes me to the fact that the service is over.

I spot Tamara leaving the rostrum and go over to her. She leads me to a small room and we sit facing each other.

'He's here,' she says. 'He wants you to know it's not your fault. You're not to blame. He was on a self-destructive journey. It was his lifestyle that caused his death, not you.' She smiles. 'He wants you to know he loved you.' She stops speaking, nods her head and says, 'Yes, I will. I'll tell her.

'To prove he's with you, he will move a picture. It will happen in the next couple of days. The picture he moves will have some significance.'

She sits with her eyes closed, as though in prayer. I want her to say his name, to tell me he played a fiddle, to give me the proof I need. The seconds tick by but the words don't come and I quietly stand up and leave the room...

'...If she'd said his name or mentioned his fiddle, I wouldn't have a shred of doubt. Music was the key thing in Sean's life.'

'Not as important as alcohol,' says Alice.

'She didn't mention his drinking.'

'She did,' says Lydia. 'When she said she felt giddy I knew she was talking about Sean.'

My eyes are alert, never far from scanning the walls. The weekend comes to an end and no picture has been moved. My visitors get ready to leave while I walk around the house, checking to make sure they've left nothing behind. I go into the dining room and immediately say, 'How did that happen?'

'What?' says Alice, coming into the room.

I point to the mermaid. 'Can you see it's been moved?'

'I haven't touched it, and the children wouldn't be able to reach that high.'

'One of us probably knocked it without knowing,' says Lydia.

I put the frame straight, thinking she's probably right.

I help take the luggage to the car, watch them drive away and go back into the house. I walk from room to room, looking at every picture, print, painting and photograph. Nothing is out of place.

Ilfracombe has more than its fair share of seagulls. The cries of the birds start at daybreak – there's no need for alarm clocks. I push back the bed covers and, not bothering with slippers, go down the stairs. I'm walking past the dining room when I suddenly stop. What I see draws me into the room. The mermaid and her frame have turned forty degrees, have been moved with such a force, shells that once decorated the frame are scattered across the floor.

I pick up the shells, wondering how it could possibly be. There's no one here but me. I put the shells onto the table, thinking about Sean and all that has happened – Sean and I in that strange ochre land, the car flashing its headlights, beeping its horn as though it were alive, the little pipit following me around the garden – and now the mermaid. The collage could not possibly move by itself. Tamara had said a significant picture; there's no other picture more significant than this one. I put my hand on the frame and straighten it, remembering Tamara's words – 'You're not to blame. He wants you to know he loved you,' and suddenly I feel free.

I go to the doorway, stop to look at my mermaid, trying to remember if it was I that put the smile on her face.

Thank you for reading **Skylark** – I hope you enjoyed it!

If so, I would really appreciate it if you could share with friends and leave reviews.

You may also like to read my first novel **Playinground** – set in the heatwave of 1976, and which has received 5* reviews.

If you would like to stay in touch, I can be contacted on Twitter @SusanHu76288306

Printed in Great Britain
by Amazon